BOEING 727

Front cover:
The first Advanced 727-200 for United Airlines seen on a test flight in 1977. *All photographs are courtesy Boeing unless otherwise credited.*

Back cover, top:
A pair of Boeing 727-200s for Royal Air Maroc fly in close formation.

Back cover, bottom:
A Boeing 727-200 series operated by Iberia prepares for yet another landing. *Allan Burney*

Below:
Delta Airlines still uses about 130 727s, most of which are relatively low-time Advanced 200-series aircraft.

MODERN CIVIL AIRCRAFT:13

BOEING 727

Peter Gilchrist

IAN ALLAN
Publishing

First published 1996
Reprinted 2000

ISBN 0 7110 2081 7

© Ian Allan Publishing Ltd 1996

Published by Ian Allan Publishing

an imprint of Ian Allan Publishing Ltd, Terminal House,
Station Approach, Shepperton, Surrey TW17 8AS.

Distributed in the United States of America by Plymouth
Press, 101 Panton Road, Vergennes, VT 05491
Call: (800) 477-2398 or (802) 877-2150

Printed by Ian Allan Printing Ltd, Riverdene Business Park,
Hersham, Surrey KT12 4RG.

Code: 0004/2

Acknowledgements

The author would like to thank Capt Dave Peet
for his invaluable technical advice; Dr Hugh
Newell and Paul K. Thompson for historical and
photographic research; Dr Steve Foster for
most of the line drawings; John Roach and Tony
Eastwood for permission to extract and use the
production data, and SW in Somerset, for her
tireless support through many difficult
moments.

Contents:

Below:
The Danish charter specialist Sterling Airways was the
first carrier to adopt the Valsan 'Quiet 727' concept in
1989, which involved changing the two outer engines and
fitting a hush-kit to the third (see page 70). *Hugh Newell*

1: Developing a Winner

Above:
Lufthansa was the first overseas customer for 727s.
Hugh Newell

When Boeing engineers started work on the 727 programme in the mid-1950s, the projects office in Seattle was under no illusions about the magnitude of the problems that lay ahead. A huge potential market was available for the first successful short-range jet, but most of the big names in the industry were understandably nervous about taking on such a specialised commitment, because preliminary studies had shown just how difficult it would be to put together a winning design. The aerodynamic and operational demands of a local-service airliner were significantly more challenging than anything encountered during development of the first generation of long-haul jets, and in the aircraft business, any kind of technical uncertainty has always represented a frightening degree of commercial risk.

All the major problems were directly related to the proposed route structure. Any long-haul airliner spends 90% of its flight time cruising in straight lines at very high altitudes, and this predictable operating environment gives the development team a clear priority for all the aerodynamic and systems trade-offs that have to be made during the early project phase. Every aspect of a long-range jet is focused on the requirement for efficient, economical cruising, and all other modes of flight — take-off, climb-out, let-down and landing-approach — are, to some extent, subservient to the cruise condition in the general order of things. Fuel costs are all-important on long, intercontinental routes, and savings of half a per cent in the cruise are pursued vigorously during development, because such tiny margins make a big difference over the working life-time of an aircraft. The task of a long-haul designer is also made slightly easier by the knowledge that big airliners operate almost exclusively from well-equipped, international airports, which generally have long runways to accommodate high landing and take-off speeds, and excellent ground-based facilities for handling both the aircraft and its payload.

Contrasting requirements
None of this would be true for the proposed 'bus-stop' airliner, and all sides of industry

Above:
Air Canada bought its first 727s in late 1973, originally for a shuttle-type operation between Toronto and Montreal. They are still used extensively for domestic passenger services, and for routes deep into the United States. This 727-233 (C-GAAF) is seen at Houston International Airport in Texas. *Peter Gilchrist*

quickly realised that such an aircraft would never be able to share the day-to-day operating advantages of its longer-range cousins. Cruising efficiency would still be important to its overall economics, but on routes that measured in tens or hundreds of miles, rather than thousands, the short-haul aircraft would spend very little of its time at the kind of super-economy altitudes enjoyed by the big jets. Instead, it would normally be required to cruise in the comparatively rough air between 20-25,000ft, and on the very shortest of routes it would certainly be lower than that — perhaps even below 10,000ft. For each sector flown, the inefficient climb and descent phases would occupy a much greater proportion of the total flight time, and the majority of routes would start and finish at small municipal airports. At that time — even in the United States — these secondary fields were often poorly equipped, with short runways and only a limited range of approach aids.

No short-range jet could escape these the start operating limitations, and it was obvious from the start that uncompromised fuel economy in the cruise would not contribute much to its overall profitability. An airline management was far more likely to be impressed by a 10min saving on the minimum achievable turnaround time, or perhaps a promise of good dispatch reliability, because both of these could be translated into extra revenue-earning sectors at the end of a busy day. A high maximum landing weight would certainly be needed to enable the aircraft to fly several sectors without refuelling, and fast climb and descent rates were necessary to achieve cruising altitude quickly, and then let down again as close as possible to the destination — perhaps into the complex traffic pattern of a so-called 'village' airport, where the approach aids might be more suited to the handling of light trainers and business-twins. To avoid attracting punitive airport charges, the new jet would have to be capable of slotting into a varied tapestry of local traffic with the minimum of disturbance, which would obviously need a much slower than average approach speed. The speed and accuracy of the touchdown would ultimately dictate the aircraft's stopping distance on the runway, and this in turn would govern its accessibility to many of the smaller airfields dotted around the world. One thing was quite certain: the more communities this aircraft could serve, the more profitable it would be for everyone.

Financial gamble

Before going too far into the project, Boeing had to look very carefully at its own financial and technical resources, which were already being stretched almost to the limit by the burgeoning KC-135/707 programme. When the first short-range studies began in February 1956, the KC-97 and B-47 production lines were both drawing to a close (at Renton and Wichita respectively), and the B-52 programme was in full swing at Seattle and Wichita. The only jet transport flying anywhere in the United States at that time was the privately-funded Model 367-80 — Seattle's hand-built precursor to the entire KC-135/707 family.

An initial US Air Force contract for tanker/transport developments of 'Dash-80' had been secured in October 1954, and this had been followed by enough repeat business to keep the line going for several years. Tooling for large-scale production at Renton, however, had been an expensive operation, and flight testing of the first military example was not due to begin until the late summer of 1956. The company would then have to undertake a lengthy clearance and acceptance programme (the US Air Force equivalent of FAA certification) before

delivery payments became available in any meaningful numbers.

On the commercial front, Pan American had placed a pioneering order for 707 Stratoliners in October 1955, but construction of the first aircraft was still some way off (it would eventually fly on 20 December 1957). In the meantime, the marketing people at Seattle had accepted deposits from other airlines for several different versions of the same basic airframe, and by the end of 1955 the factory was committed to building 707s with three different engine types, two fuselage lengths and at least two major wing changes. In the projects office, initial engineering work had also started on the derivative medium-range Model 717 (later to become the Boeing 720), which would soon generate yet another wing planform and a third fuselage length. These variants had all been agreed by Boeing in order to give the 707 a wide customer base, but each new revision distorted the normal learning-curve, which delayed break-even point on the whole programme. Under these circumstances, it was impossible in 1956 to make any firm commitment towards full-scale development of yet another design, but work on various aspects of the short-range project continued throughout the year, and by the beginning of 1957 more than 40 engineers were involved in the studies.

The high-lift wing

It had been clear from the beginning of the 727

7

Above:
The 3,000th commercial jet manufactured by Boeing was this Advanced 727-200 (N284US) – which was actually airframe number 1,284 from the Renton tri-jet line. The aircraft was rolled out with considerable celebration in July 1977, and delivered to Northwest Orient (now Northwest Airlines) on 9 August.

programme that efficient cruising flight at the proposed lower altitudes would need a small, highly loaded wing, with sufficient flexibility in the structure to provide an adequate standard of passenger comfort in 'bumpy' weather. This part of the specification was fine as far as it went, and was easily achievable within the constraints of existing knowledge and techniques, but the cruising requirement was diametrically opposed to the large, lightly-loaded surface needed for slow approach speeds. One of the early aims of the study programme had been to produce an aircraft of around 135,000lb gross weight, which would be capable of taking-off without payload penalty from a 5-6,000ft runway. It was certain that a small wing would never achieve this target without the help of a powerful high-lift system, so most of the research effort was switched during 1957 into low-speed aerodynamics, in an attempt to find the highest attainable coefficient of lift with the least possible weight and mechanical complexity.

A lot of basic high-lift research had already been done at Seattle as part of a programme to improve the airfield performance of the KC-135 and 707, and the scope of this work was quickly expanded to encompass the proposed short-range aircraft. Starting from a coefficient of lift (clean) of about 1.25, the new studies initially focused on an absolute value of 1.8 in the landing configuration. As time went by, experience with the available high-lift systems greatly improved, and the target figure was increased to 2.2 at the end of 1957, and then raised again to 2.5 during 1958. Several hundred different combinations of leading and trailing-edge devices were examined during this period, most of them in somewhat cursory fashion, but others in considerable detail. The most promising theoretical configurations were assembled in model form for tunnel testing, and one or two ideas later progressed into flight-approved hardware for trials aboard 'Dash-80' — which, by that time, was being used as a general research mount for Boeing development programmes. Aerofoils were tunnel tested with various arrangements of Krueger flaps (flat ramp-like panels designed to hinge down and forward from the underside of the leading-edge, effectively increasing both the chord and camber of the wing): powered slat sections (miniature aerofoils that fit like a glove around the leading-edge for cruising flight, but deploy forwards and downwards at low speed, leaving a flow-stabilising slot to re-energise the airflow over the outer wing panels); and double and triple-slotted Fowler-type flaps, which extend from the trailing-edge to increase the chord and camber of the wing, and provide a substantial degree of controllable drag to slow the aircraft down. At one time the programme even examined the possibility of incorporating a system of fully 'blown' flaps, which would make use of accurately directed jets of high-pressure engine bleed air to augment the flow over the basic surfaces, and also to smooth out the flow over drag-producing surfaces such as the flap operating mechanisms.

There was no single, ideal solution to the problem of low approach speeds, so the high-lift programme became a long and immensely complicated affair. All the deployable surfaces would have subtle aerodynamic effects on each other, and differences in their size, profile and relative positions on the wing gave the design engineers an almost infinitely variable range of possibilities. The initial work — mainly a process of elimination — was time-consuming and tedious, but during the first few months of 1959 a clear pattern of relationships between the various surfaces began to emerge, and early computers were brought in to handle most of the mathematical modelling. These machines dramatically improved the effectiveness of the programme, and the accuracy of their predictive calculations soon allowed the minimum runway-length target to be brought down from 5,000ft to only 4,500ft. The investigation entered its final phase when all the theoretical work was transferred into the model shop and wind tunnel. Then, over the next 12 months, more than 450 hours of tunnel time were devoted solely to the process of selecting the combination of surfaces to be used, and refining the system to achieve the highest possible level of performance. The final 727 wing — which was the first in the world to use triple-slotted flaps — was widely acknowledged as a masterpiece of the aerodynamicist's art. It certainly exceeded its original coefficient of lift target by a handsome margin, and has subsequently survived the most punishing of flight regimes without any significant fatigue or corrosion problems.

Configuration questions

While the wing was being finalised, a second team of engineers was looking at the overall configuration of the aircraft, trying to establish the optimum fuselage size, and laying-out positions for all the major components. Most of the early studies appear to have favoured a 'baby' version of the 707. This would certainly have been the simplest aircraft of all to build, because much of the structural engineering could have been directly adapted from the 707 itself. Four engines though, suggested a considerable investment in future maintenance, and some of the parallel twin-engined studies were already showing a 5-8% improvement in

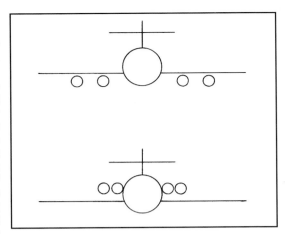

Above:
Of the four-engined studies, the most promising were 'baby' versions of the VC10 and 707. (All drawings are schematic representations of the engine layouts only; the position and dihedral angle of both wing and tail varied considerably between actual proposals.)

operating economics. A three-engined design was also suggested, but this idea was not seriously considered until about 18 months into the study programme.

Of the four-engined proposals, two that achieved some prominence were the Models 727-474 and 475. The engines of the 474 were mounted in side-by-side pairs on the rear fuselage, in a style later adopted by Vickers for the VC10: the horizontal tail was initially mounted low on the fin, but well aft of the engines and with marked dihedral to keep it clear of the exhaust plume. The fuselage was basically adapted from that of the emerging 720, with main landing-gear bays in the wing/body intersection. Subsequent revisions of the design moved the tailplane closer to the top of the fin, and transferred the main undercarriage units into Kuchemann-style 'speed-pods' at about 40% of the semi-span. Although the general arrangement of the 474 was aerodynamically acceptable, Boeing engineers were uneasy about using closely-coupled engine pods on a commercial aircraft because of the risk of contagious engine failure (one engine ingesting debris from its twin). Military feedback from the B-47 and B-52 programmes also suggested that even experienced pilots regularly shut down a good engine — or at least reduced its thrust — if the pod-partner suffered an unexplained failure. Such caution was probably acceptable on a six or eight-engined military jet, but not on a four-engined airliner.

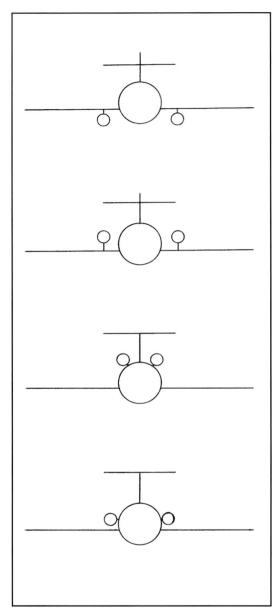

Above:
Twin-engined studies included low, mid and T-tails, and some of the proposals incorporated a special wide-track undercarriage.

The 727-475 was entirely conventional in every way. Using a very similar wing planform and structure to the Model 474, it had four widely separated engines, mounted on pylons to position them below and slightly ahead of the leading-edge. In general layout this was as close as the short-range project ever came to the

'baby' 707 concept — although in reality it used a cut-down version of the Boeing 720 fuselage (102ft long instead of the 720's 136ft). The wing was positioned further forward than that of the 707 or 720, but the fuselage cross-section was common to all three aircraft, and the tails bore a strong family resemblance both in form and control-function. The commercial risks of using such a conventional layout were fairly low, but the aircraft itself was too close to the 720 in virtually every aspect of its accommodation and performance — indeed, it was even nicknamed the '720 Junior' for a while.

Twin-engined proposals
The four-engined studies were all based on the unproven 8,250lb thrust Pratt & Whitney JTF10A turbofan, but the proposed twins needed much more take-off power from each engine, so they were designed to use either the 16,500lb Rolls-Royce Conway RCo.10, or the 17,000lb Pratt & Whitney JT3D — both of which had already been ordered in some numbers to power different variants of the 707. All the 727 projects had broadly similar power-to-weight ratios, but the design team was always alert to the fact that any powerplant failure on one of the twins would cut the thrust by 50%. This was obviously more serious than the loss of one out of four engines, but it was still safe in terms of reserve power, and the aircraft would remain fully controllable providing the engines were positioned correctly.

The natural inclination at Seattle was to use underwing pods whenever possible, but in order to guarantee satisfactory asymmetric handling, the powerplants of a twin would have to be positioned very close to the aircraft centreline — much closer, in fact, than the inboard pods of a four-engined design. This was feasible on a technical level, but it threatened to expose the low-slung engines to slush and debris thrown up by the nosewheel, and the proximity of the nacelles to the fuselage would certainly obstruct easy access to all passenger and cargo doors ahead of the wing. One of the last of a number of proposals based on this layout was the Model 265, which was virtually a twin-engined version of the 727-475. From a purely engineering point of view, this aircraft had a number of positive advantages: it would probably have been much easier to build than most of the alternative twins, and because it used the same engines as the 707, the pods and pylons — and perhaps even some of the engine control systems and internal wing structure — might have been made common to both types. The operational

problems however — particularly the case of take-offs and landings on a slush-covered runway — caused nagging doubts about possible engine damage, and the design was shelved while other ideas were considered.

Much of the subsequent investigation was designed to move the engines away from the area immediately alongside the forward fuselage. One of the more original schemes was to put the pods on top of the wing, mounted on swept pylons to position the powerplants directly over the trailing-edge. This configuration solved the ingestion problem and allowed uncluttered access to the forward doors, but the thrust line still had to be well inboard, which put the engines far too close to the occupied section of the passenger cabin. Carrying this general idea one stage further, a version called the Model 257 incorporated podded engines mounted high on the rear fuselage, similar in many ways to the installation later used by Bill Lear for his range of business jets. This improved the thrust line and avoided the problem of having potentially explosive powerplants directly alongside the cabin, but the pressure shell had to be shortened slightly to accommodate the engine mountings, which wasted internal space and reduced the passenger capacity by a couple of seat rows.

This layout also made the engines difficult to reach for routine maintenance, and the raised exhaust plume complicated the tail geometry. On the later Model 264, most of these flaws were corrected by moving the engines right to the back of the fuselage, and bringing them down from the 'shoulder' position, to more convenient mountings immediately aft of the rearmost passenger window. A similar layout had already been flown successfully on the SE.210 Caravelle, and variations of it were later adopted by almost every business jet and twin-engined airliner. Several versions of the 264 were studied by Boeing, including models with low, mid and T-tails: some of these designs also incorporated the 474-style wide-track undercarriage, with the main trucks retracting into wing-mounted pods.

The tri-jet emerges

The possibility of adopting a three-engined configuration was considered at an early stage in the programme, but the discussions were not taken too far because it was difficult to match available engine power to the proposed operating weight of the aircraft. It was clear that a trio of JTF10s would not be able to provide enough thrust to meet the take-off requirement, and the Conway and JT3D were both too big and too powerful to be used in groups of three. British industry was working on a number of suitable engines, but the range of US-designed alternatives was virtually zero, because the

Pentagon — which was largely responsible for funding powerplant development at that time — had no immediate requirement for a commercial-type engine beyond the JT3D.

During the latter half of 1957 several outside influences on the programme began to change, and interest in the tri-jet proposal was gradually revived. As part of its careful preparation for a new design, Boeing had conducted a year-long survey of weather-related departure delays in the New York area, and the results were plotted against the Federal Aviation Authority's published operating minima for two and four-engined aircraft. More than 11,000 departures were recorded, all conducting scheduled passenger services for the same airline. At Idlewild (now John F. Kennedy) Airport, twin-engined operations were restricted to a 300ft minimum cloudbase and a runway visual range of half a mile — but four-engined aircraft were cleared to continue take-offs and landings down to a cloudbase of 200ft. There were no special rules for three-engined aircraft, but the FAA agreed to recognise their improved safety margins and grant them access to the lower minima. During the year under review, no fewer than 342 twin-engined departures (more than 3% of the total) were delayed solely by weather conditions for periods of one hour or more: of these, 221 went on to be further delayed by at least two hours. When these figures were compared with the more relaxed minima for multi-engined aircraft, it was found that only 126 departures would have been delayed in the first place, and only 38 of those would have remained grounded for the full two hours. The difference in the initial delays represented 216 'lost' departures that could have been operated quite normally by a three-engined 727.

The results of this survey clearly undermined the apparent cost benefits of a twin-engined aircraft — especially for use on a network of multi-stage routes, where a single weather-related delay would have an immediate knock-on effect all the way down the line. Regular travellers were almost resigned to the occasional long delay on a transcontinental route, but a short-range jet would be used rather like an inter-city bus, and even a short delay on a scheduled 30min flight would begin to irritate passengers very quickly. In the highly competitive US market, frequent delays could do untold damage to the reputation of an airline, and in the long term this would be reflected in sales of the aircraft. The survey convinced Boeing that the extra cost of developing a tri-jet would be more than repaid in terms of departure reliability, but nothing could be done to fix the design unless a suitable engine could be found.

The initial conversion to expensive jet-engined aircraft was undertaken with considerable caution by most of the world's airlines, but as the end of the 1950s approached an increasing number of them bowed under competitive pressures, and order-books for the 707, DC-8, Comet 4 and Caravelle began to fill up rapidly. The emergence of this buoyant market was certainly noticed by the big US powerplant manufacturers, and for the first time since the advent of jets, they appeared to be willing to reduce their dependence on cozy military contracts, and risk their own stockholders' money on the development of specialised commercial engines — something the British industry had been doing for several years. This change of heart by the Americans was exceptionally well-timed for 727 programme.

In the absence of a home-grown alternative, Boeing had already been looking overseas for a suitable engine, and by the beginning of 1958 was negotiating a deal with Rolls-Royce for a licence-produced version of the 14,300lb thrust RB.141 turbofan. The increasing level of interest by US companies brought a much-needed element of competition into the equation, and Seattle skilfully played one side off against the other, until the 727 project team was virtually allowed to write its own engine specification. No commitments were entered into at that stage, but Pratt & Whitney (already a preferred supplier of 707 engines) agreed to begin preliminary work on a new 14,000lb thrust turbofan, which was loosely based on the J52 military core.

Tri-jet configurations

The promised availability of two ideally-sized turbofans gave Boeing the opportunity to take a much closer look at possible tri-jet

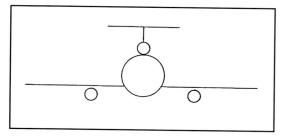

Right:
Most of the early tri-jet studies featured wing-mounted pods for the outer engines.

configurations. Using a new series of model-numbers beginning with 727-301 (three engines/project 01), the design team investigated the structural and aerodynamic performance of a wide range of options, including some with all three engines mounted internally, and others based wholly or mainly on external pods. One of the early projects centred on a one-up/two-down triangular arrangement inside the rear fuselage, with the engines fed by annular scoop or flush-mounted boundary-layer intakes, and exhausted through separate pipes in the tail. This appeared to be a neat and aerodynamically clean solution, with all three engines close to the aircraft centreline; but the routine maintenance of closely-packed engines was an obvious drawback, and the risk of contagious engine failure was even more severe on this layout than it was on the rejected 727-474. Another shortlived proposal involved two podded engines on one side of the rear fuselage, and only one on the other! This curious concept appears to have been suggested as a means of avoiding a complicated tail structure, but it clearly lacked the visual sophistication expected of a modern, high-performance airliner, and might easily have become the butt of much unwelcome humour. The idea was probably worth considering on a purely academic level, and may even have worked tolerably well, but in the absence of any spectacular advantages it was soon shelved in favour of more conventional layouts.

Although several strange, new configurations were investigated, it was accepted almost from the start of tri-jet studies that one of the engines would have to be mounted on the aircraft centreline — and the only sensible place to put this was at the rear of the fuselage, either inside the main body structure or mounted on the tail in some previously untried way. The two outer powerplants could be installed almost anywhere, providing they were in matching positions on each side of the aircraft.

Most of the early studies featured underwing pods for the outer engines: these were generally combined with a central pod on the upper fuselage, or with an S-duct leading to an internal rear engine. The existence of the third power unit greatly reduced the severity of any asymmetric problems, so the wing pods on a tri-jet could always be located further away from the fuselage than those on a twin. This allowed relatively free movement around the forward passenger and baggage doors, and shifted the inlets way from the danger area immediately behind the nosewheel. The triangular disposition of engines around the centre-of-gravity provided a much better basic balance than any of the alternative layouts (which eased the task of internal load distribution), and all three nacelles were reasonably accessible for routine maintenance. For some time, this configuration was strongly fancied by the project team, but a more detailed assessment exposed several flaws in its structural efficiency. Although the forward engines had been moved outboard, they were still too close to the fuselage to provide any useful relief against wing bending stresses, and the structure of the wing itself had to be heavier than expected in order to counteract the torsional loads imposed by pods on its leading edge. Also, with the three power units so widely separated, all the essential cables, pipes, ducts and control mechanisms — most of which needed frequent mechanical support from a wide range of clips and fasteners — were much longer than they really needed to be. This added unnecessary weight to the aircraft, and the multitude of valves and connectors required by such a complex system threatened to overwhelm the maintenance procedures.

The rear-engined option

Moving all three engines into the tail area, above and behind the wing, seemed to make good aerodynamic and structural sense. The tail and rear fuselage would obviously need to be heavier to bear the extra loads, but the wing would be lighter, and the problem of long pipe and cable runs was eliminated altogether. Rear engines would also make the cabin much quieter, and full reverse thrust could be used without any risk of acoustic fatigue or debris damage to the flaps. The flaps themselves, and the essential leading-edge devices, could extend across the entire span if necessary, and the undercarriage legs could be reduced in length, lowering the fuselage to make loading and refuelling slightly easier. The only apparent problem was the loss of 'natural' balance on the aircraft, which could be countered fairly easily by moving the wing back towards the tail. Maintenance access to the outer engines would also be slightly more difficult, but their inlets would certainly be better protected against stone damage.

Tail layout

The design of the tail occupied a considerable amount of study time, with several variations tried before the classic-T finally emerged. Under the model number 727-323, a lot of early work was done on butterfly tails. This could have been the perfect choice in many ways because the V-structure lent itself nicely to the provision of a centre engine — either podded on top of the upper fuselage, or buried inside the main body with a scoop intake above. The two outer engines would fit symmetrically on the sides of the rear fuselage, directly beneath the sloping tail surfaces. This neat arrangement seemed absolutely ideal, until someone in the design office remembered the bleak prospect of an airport in conditions of heavy snow or rain: the angled slabs of a V-tail formed a highly-efficient sluice, which would carry copious amounts of

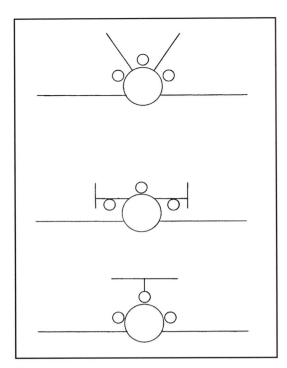

Top:
The V-tail was a tempting concept, but it had problems in bad weather.

Middle:
Several variations of the end-plate tail were considered.

Bottom:
The T-tail was ideal for the 727, although the structure was difficult to build.

slush and water straight into the operating mechanism below. Unless this could be drained adequately (which was unlikely), it would cause long-term corrosion damage inside the fuselage, and freeze solid at high altitudes, possibly jamming the flight controls.

The butterfly proposal was abandoned with much reluctance, and attention briefly switched to a B-24 Liberator-style tail, with twin end-plate fins on a transverse-beam stabiliser. This again allowed the centre engine to be mounted internally or externally, but it left a difficult choice for the two outer engines. If they were mounted on the fuselage sides beneath the tail, they would again be vulnerable to any debris scuffed up from the runway (this time from the mainwheels), and the tail surfaces themselves might be damaged by stones or acoustic fatigue whenever reverse thrust was used. The only practical alternative was to raise the pods and attach them directly to the upper or lower surfaces of the horizontal tail. This would at least allow the reverser gases to pass above and below the actual stabilizer, but the size and power of the elevators would certainly be compromised by the need to accommodate the two tailpipes, and the tailplane itself would have to be a fixed surface, and therefore not available for trimming the aircraft.

A number of T-tailed configurations were tested during the period of twin-engined studies, and it was only a matter of time before they found their way on to the tri-jet programme. The idea was resisted at first because of the difficulty of carrying all the structural loads around the centre engine, but the more it was investigated, the more attractive the proposal became. The big advantage of the T-tail was that it shifted the horizontal stabilizer way above the normal aerodynamic influence of the wing, and at the same time protected it from damage caused by the thrust-reversers. Several military aircraft (notably the Victor and Javelin in the UK, and F-104 and P6M in the United States) had already demonstrated the basic integrity of the design, but it had not been used on an airliner until de Havilland announced the three-engined DH.121 (later the Trident) in February 1958.

The Trident proposal

The Trident and the 727 were both designed to meet broadly similar specification — although in the case of the Trident the commissioning customer (British European Airways) virtually dictated the number of powerplants before the project began, and this channelled most of the research effort straight into three-engined configurations. The Boeing design evolved rather more slowly, through the initial four-engined studies, into twins, and then into the tri-jet phase during late 1957 and early 1958. Ultimately faced with the same set of problems, it was fairly obvious that competent engineers on both sides of the Atlantic would arrive at very similar solutions — or at least, it *should* have been fairly obvious!

As we now know, the engine, intake and tail geometry finally chosen for the 727 was remarkably similar to that of the Trident — so similar in fact, that several ill-informed European newspapers lashed out at Boeing and virtually accused the Americans of technical plagiarism. With the benefit of hindsight (and especially in the light of so many modern design similarities) we can now see these indignant attacks as wholly unjustified, but in 1960, when the British aircraft was still being praised for its innovative ideas and almost eccentrically unique layout, the passions developed by first sight of the 727 were perhaps more understandable. It seems likely that the 'copying' theory was raised because Boeing had been given details of the Trident some months before the tail configuration of the 727 was finalised. A technical mission from Hatfield also went to Seattle about a year before the 727 was announced, in an attempt to form some kind of Anglo/US alliance on the short-range jet programme. It was suggested by de Havilland that a second Trident assembly line be set up in the United States: that way, it was argued, both sides would benefit by not having to compete for orders, and Boeing in particular could avoid further risk to its hard-pressed resources by

Below:
Delta has been operating 727-200s since the early 1970s, and is now one of the biggest users of the type. N409DA was delivered in January 1976, and still flies regular domestic services from its Atlanta base.
Peter Gilchrist

dropping the unfinished 727.

In those days Boeing was still predominantly a military (bombers and tankers) business, with a 'small' commercial aircraft division that was forecast to lose about $1 million on every 707 it produced: much work still had to be done on the 727, which was anything up to a year behind the Trident in terms of detail design. Boeing then was far from being the confident world leader it has since become, and the Hatfield proposal was treated seriously because it represented a ready-made programme with predictable costs, and at that time the aircraft itself was fairly close to the ideas emerging from the Seattle project office. The paperwork submissions were examined in considerable detail, and although the quality of the Trident clearly impressed Boeing engineers, the aircraft as it stood was unable to meet the requirements of several major customers. Most of the important US airlines needed something with a 5,000ft runway capability, but the de Havilland aircraft (designed as it was for scheduled services between well-equipped European airports) had no requirement for such a short take-off, and was limited at full load to a runway length of about 6,000ft. Fitting the British aircraft with a version of the American high-lift wing might have solved some of the

problems, but the two designs were never structurally compatible, and the subsequent re-engineering effort would have been as costly to Boeing as continuing with the 727.

The rejection of the Trident came as no great surprise to de Havilland, but the mission itself had been a worthwhile exercise, and much had been learned by both sides during the discussions. Hatfield later dismissed all the fuss about design similarities by reminding detractors that Boeing had the best wind tunnel resources in the world, and a team of aerodynamicists and engineers who were more than capable of establishing a successful layout for themselves.

Parametric study

In parallel with all the technical work on the 727, a wide-ranging parametric survey was conducted by the financial, operations and marketing disciplines at Seattle. This extensive investigation looked at virtually every aspect of designing, manufacturing, operating and maintaining a short-range jet aircraft, and tried to keep ahead of developments in all the peripheral fields that might have some bearing on the direction of the programme. The New York traffic figures, for instance, were gathered and analysed as part of this survey, and other key elements included an investigation of the possible effects of future airport development in the United States, with particular reference to changes in runway length, air traffic control procedures, and advanced instrumentation which could lead to the general adoption of automatic landing techniques. All the existing or projected powerplants were examined for their suitability on two, three and four-engined projects, and a unified method of costing their operational and maintenance schedules was established, enabling much more accurate comparisons to be made between the various options. Airport and routeing restrictions were also investigated, together with all the operating minima laid down at national (FAA), local, or even individual airline level. The complete survey occupied thousands of man-hours and delved into many previously unresearched areas, but the background information it gathered was invaluable to the 727 programme, and provided much of the day-to-day confidence needed to see the project through.

Customer reaction

Surprisingly, the tri-jet proposal was not discussed in any great detail with potential customers until the summer of 1959. By then Boeing engineers knew exactly what kind of

Below:
Iberia is now the largest European operator of 727s. This 200-series aircraft (EC-CBF) was delivered new to Madrid over 20 years ago, and is likely to remain there in regular service until noise or fatigue make further operations impossible. *Hugh Newell*

aircraft they wanted to build, but the boardroom had reservations about the three-engined concept, which might not have been accepted by the airlines quite so readily as a straightforward twin or four-engined design. Reassurances were certainly needed on this important point, and before the programme went too far a number of fundamental questions had to be answered — such as how many seats the aircraft should have, and what its ideal range and performance limits should be. Any basic mistakes at that stage could have had colossal implications for Boeing's future, so the company president, William M. Allen, toured the offices of all the major US airlines between June and September 1959, making presentations of individual design ideas and seeking opinions that would finally shape the production aircraft.

Several airlines visited by Allen had already received a Trident briefing from de Havilland, and most of them were agreeably receptive to the tri-jet proposal. Eastern, Capital and Pan American actually expressed a preference for three engines, while American, Braniff, TWA and United varied in wanting either a twin or a four-engined aircraft as their first choice, but all four were more than happy to consider an economical tri-jet. At least two of the airlines said they would definitely not buy a twin for busy short-range routes, and another refused (primarily on cost grounds) to consider anything with four engines. From Boeing's point of view, the most satisfying result of the tour was that none of the US 'big seven' had rejected the tri-

Above:
Tunis Air has operated 727-200s since the early 1970s, but with A320s now in service it seems certain that the tri-jet's days are numbered. TS-JHQ was first delivered in November 1974. *Hugh Newell*

jet out of hand.

The airlines with the largest domestic route networks were American, Eastern, TWA and United. All four were seen as prime targets for 727 launch orders, and each was offered a powerful voice in determining the final size, weight and performance of the aircraft. Eastern and United both wanted a short-range jet almost immediately, and their basic requirements were very similar: both wanted 114-120 tourist-class seats in a six-abreast cabin; both suggested a maximum range of 1,500nm; and both insisted on an aircraft that could operate at full load from La Guardia's short (4,980ft) runway 4/22. TWA on the other hand, needed a jet to replace its ageing fleet of piston-engined Martin 4-0-4s, but it really wanted a slightly smaller, twin-engined aircraft, with a range of about 1,000nm: the Boeing tri-jet might have done the job, but an early order seemed out of the question because the company was desperately short of cash following its ill-timed acquisition of 30 Convair 880s. American Airlines was potentially the biggest prize of all, but it too liked the idea of a smaller twin, and showed little immediate interest in a three-engined 727 — preferring instead, to believe that its newly-acquired Lockheed Electras could handle all the short-range traffic into the foreseeable future.

Detail design
More than 60 different configurations had been

considered during the three-year study phase, but the T-tailed tri-jet seemed to be an aircraft that most airlines would accept. Favourable comments filtering back from Bill Allen's grand tour gave senior managers much more confidence in the project, and in June 1959 approval was given to start the detailed design work. A 148in wide fuselage cross-section (based on the 707) was chosen, and construction of the first of three engineering mock-ups to this pattern was initiated at the beginning of July. During this busy period the number of people working solely on the 727 increased to over 100 for the first time, and the work itself became much more focused, with the selection and positioning of major components completed by the end of July, and the final choice of materials specifications following at the end of August. Boeing has often quoted 18 September 1959 as the design completion date, but the choice of engine was delayed for at least another year, so the word 'completion' has to be understood in its basic aerodynamic and structural sense.

Right up until mid-October 1960, it was evident that the project team wanted a developed version of the 12,750lb thrust Rolls-Royce RB.163 (Spey) as lead powerplant on the 727, but US airlines still preferred the 'safe' option of a home-produced Pratt & Whitney JT8D. Both engines were little more than paper projects at that time, but the production Spey was designed to be some 700lb lighter than its American rival, and have a much smaller diameter (37in, compared with the JT8D's 42.5in). The power output and specific fuel consumption figures were broadly comparable, but the smaller Spey would have saved structural weight on the airframe and reduced drag from the nacelles.

It seemed certain that the JT8D would have to be available for any airline that wanted it, but the benefits offered by the British engine prompted Boeing to look at the possibility of a separate, 'international' version of the aircraft. This would be assembled on the same production line as the domestic model, but be powered by Speys manufactured in, and entirely supported from, the United States: in this all-American guise, the RB.163 would have become the Allison/Rolls-Royce AR-963. Unfortunately the British team failed to recognise the enormous potential of this arrangement. Derby was reluctant to allow key components of the engine to be manufactured under licence, and the UK Government refused to finance any of the essential investment in Allison's Indianapolis factory. Such parochial attitudes simply confirmed the US airlines' worst fears about divided loyalties under such a contract, and Eastern, at least, refused to have anything to do with a 727 powered by 'domesticated' versions of a foreign engine. Several other carriers followed Eastern's lead, and Boeing was increasingly forced into an exclusive Pratt & Whitney camp. The proposed licensing deal between Allison and Rolls-Royce was allowed to wither and die, and the Spey was dropped from the programme altogether towards the end of 1960.

Qualified support

Jack Steiner, the brilliant engineer who had masterminded the 727 programme almost since its inception, presented the final design to Boeing directors at a specially convened meeting during February 1960. The accumulated losses on the 707 programme up to the end of 1959 had just been confirmed at $200 million, which inevitably soured the atmosphere and made it a bad time to talk about yet another commercial product. The board as a whole was understandably nervous about the level of investment needed to get the 727 going, but Bill Allen — still fresh from his optimistic talks with the 'big seven' US airlines — gave Steiner his personal backing, and promised to continue development work until at least the end of the year.

The initial tooling costs alone for the tri-jet programme were assessed at well over $100 million, and break-even point on the entire research, development and production effort was privately estimated at between 220 and 240 aircraft. Before the crucial board meeting, a market survey commissioned by Seattle suggested that up to 500 727-type jets would be needed by the free world's airlines before the end of 1965, and if traffic continued to develop as expected, a further 500 would be ordered by the end of 1970. Of these, Boeing could reasonably expect to sell about 150 aircraft in the first five-year period, and up to 400 by the end of the decade. These figures looked promising enough in the longer term, but it was patently obvious that any large-scale investment in the 727 would not be returned in the form of profits until 1966-67 at the earliest. In the meantime money had to be found from

Below:
Originally delivered to National Airlines in February 1965, this 100-series aircraft was purchased by the US Air Force as C-22A, 83-4616. *Hugh Newell*

somewhere, which could possibly result in a new equity plan or extensive borrowing. Either way, continuation of the programme was an enormous gamble, and Bill Allen had to be confident that he could sell at least 100 aircraft before any production commitment could be undertaken. A new meeting was planned for 1 December 1960, and the sales department was given the intervening nine months to go out and find the necessary orders.

Launch orders

Although the 727 was an expensive machine to buy (about $4 million, compared with $2.1 million for the 400mph Electra), intelligent design had certainly given it some extremely seductive operating economics. During the sales campaign much emphasis was placed on the 148in wide cabin, which guaranteed six-abreast seating in some comfort, and yielded 12% greater earning potential than all its five-abreast rivals. The cost of the bigger fuselage in terms of additional drag was less than one per cent in the cruise. This gave the 727 a direct operating cost per seat-mile (in tourist configuration) some 10% lower than that of the Electra, and an average direct cost per aircraft-mile of about $1.50 (1960 prices) over a 500 mile stage length. The advanced high-lift system also allowed the 727 access to almost every airfield capable of accepting an Electra, which would put the slower turboprop in an impossible competitive position if head-to-head rivalry developed on any route over about 300 miles.

As expected, the launch orders came from Eastern and United. Both airlines had to compromise some of their original requirements in order to reach an acceptable production standard, but the technical discussions made good progress, and substantial sales were virtually assured from mid-summer onwards. The engine contract was negotiated with Pratt & Whitney during August 1960, and at that stage the Boeing board authorised the construction of long-lead components such as undercarriage units, wing spars and some of the more difficult forgings: the final-assembly jigs were also designed, and plans were made to provide slots for the 727 in the 707 production line at Renton. The contracts with both airlines were signed in late November, and at their pre-planned meeting on 1 December the board went through the formal process of putting the 727 into production. At a press-conference on Monday 5 December, Bill Allen confirmed the existence of the orders, announced the company's decision

to go-ahead with the short-range jet, and gave first details of the planned production schedule.

In effect, each launch customer had ordered 40 aircraft, although the United Airlines contract was split 50/50 between firm orders and options — the second batch of 20 being conditional on the completion of a merger between United and Capital Airline, or upon the achievement by United of 'certain (unspecified) projected financial ratios'. The merger — which removed at least one major competitor from some of United's key routes — eventually went through on 1 June 1961. The value of the whole 80-aircraft order, including a considerable non-recurring package of spares, initial support activity, and training for both air and ground crews, was put at 'more than $350 million' (then the equivalent of £125 million), which Boeing later described as 'the largest order in the history of transport'. The production and delivery timetable was typically ambitious. Reporters were told that the first aircraft would be flying in March 1962 (just 15 months away), and deliveries to both customers would begin in late 1963. Although his 100-aircraft start-up requirement had not been achieved at that stage, Bill Allen was quietly confident about the financial success of the 727.

Gathering pace

The first two partial mock-ups of the aircraft were completed by the end of 1960. These were used throughout the development period to position hundreds of components such as pipe and cable runs, wiring looms, air ducts, internal furnishings, and even some of the more complex systems that were fundamental to the airframe but difficult to install without the aid of a fully representative, three-dimensional model. In the early stages, detail design of the aircraft was evolving almost daily. One of the first major revisions undertaken on the mock-up was the late inclusion of a Garrett-AiResearch GTC-85 auxiliary power unit in the wing/fuselage intersection. This costly system was not included in the original specification because Boeing engineers thought it was unnecessary. Customer airlines, however, were unhappy about the idea of running the central JT8D to provide power during short transit stops, and most of them insisted — wisely as Seattle now admits — on having the APU.

The first batch of engineering drawings reached the Boeing workshops in November 1960, while 3,000 miles away in East Hartford, Conneticutt, Pratt & Whitney began work on the

Above:
The Boeing Model 367-80 (known as 'Dash-80') was used extensively during the early 727 aerodynamic trials — particularly for testing the effectiveness of various leading-edge devices and flap systems. Later in the programme, an operating JT3 turbo-jet (seen here), and then a JT8D turbofan, were sequentially added to the rear fuselage to represent the 727's side-engine layout. The positional relationship between the Dash-80's wing-root and the test engine were kept as close as possible to those suggested for the new tri-jet, and much of the flight-test schedule was concentrated on achieving good inlet efficiency at high angles-of-attack. The curved jet pipe was not part of the proposed design for the 727, but merely a convenient way of keeping the JT's exhaust plume way from the 707's tail.

hand-built prototype of the JT8D. At about this time, Dash-80 was also brought into the experimental shop to have a single J57 turbojet mounted on the left-hand side of its rear fuselage. This aircraft was already fitted with 727-style triple-slotted flaps, and in March 1961 it resumed flying to conduct a series of inlet trials — testing the relationship between the flaps and the engine at various settings and speeds. These flights (which were later extended to incorporate a working JT8D turbofan) were vitally important to the 727 because any engine instability at high angles-of-attack and low speeds would have ruined the landing case on which much of the aircraft's success depended. In the event, preliminary wind-tunnel experiments had already established that the engine pods of the production tri-jet should be raised by about 24in, and the 'live' trials with Dash-80 were used mainly to confirm the theoretical results. All the necessary structural alterations to the 727 were

drafted very quickly, but construction of the first aircraft was inevitably delayed by the changes, and the planned first-flight date had to be moved forward to the autumn of 1962.

By March 1961 the first production materials were beginning to arrive in quantity at Renton, followed later in the year by hundreds of bought-in components ranging from altimeters and ash-trays to wheel-brakes and windscreen wipers: more than 500 outside manufacturers were involved in this complex supply chain, and contracts worth $85 million were let in the first year alone. A start was also made on the provision of more than 30,000 special production tools, and by the end of the year more than half of these were in place. The first actual jig for 727 sub-assembly (the fuselage bulkhead destined for station-870) was loaded during October.

At Pratt & Whitney, meanwhile, the prototype JT8D engine was installed in the Willgoos Test Laboratory, and the first bench runs were conducted in May 1961 — about a month later than originally planned. The test programme itself was then delayed by an annoying tendency for the high-pressure compressor to stall on acceleration — something that could not be tolerated in service. The underlying problem was traced and cured fairly quickly, allowing the initial 150hr endurance trials to be completed satisfactorily in December. By that time four or five development engines were available, and total running time had just exceeded 1,000hr. As the number of completed power units increased, the trials programme stabilised and began to make excellent progress, until, by the summer of

1962, it was more or less back on schedule, with about 4,000hr logged by a dozen or so engines. In May, one of the early JT8D-1s was delivered to Boeing to replace the J57 on the rear fuselage of Dash-80

Manufacturing begins

The workforce employed on the 727 programme had grown steadily since the go-ahead was announced, and by the summer of 1962 nearly 5,000 people were involved, with more being added every week. In February that year the test-rig for the flying-control system was commissioned, and in March the main systems and furnishings mock-up at Renton was opened for inspection by customers' air and cabin crews.

On the factory floor, sub-assemblies for the first fuselage centre-section were loaded into their production jig in March, just as the first wing-spar and vertical tail assembly were nearing completion. Work on the aft fuselage with its odd-looking 'horse-shoe' fairing for the centre-engine inlet, began during the early summer, and by late July it was being joined in a common production-jig to the main structural components of the fin. This entire assembly was removed from its jig in late August, and after detail finishing, it was joined to the fuselage centre-section during the first week of September. This first major sub-section (weighing several tons at that stage) was moved by overhead crane into the final assembly area, where it was lowered onto the structural part of the wing and the two were bolted together. The forward-fuselage and cockpit section was moved into position and mated during early October, giving factory staff their first clear impression of the size and shape of the finished aircraft. There then followed a mass of detailed work to prepare the 'prototype' for its busy flight-test schedule, including the installation of all on-board equipment and instrumentation; connection of hundreds of individual cables, pipes and ducts; rigging the vital flight-control system; and installing the control surfaces themselves, including the big, variable-incidence tailplane. Static test engines and all three undercarriage units were installed by the end of October, and during the first few days of November the structurally complete aircraft moved on its own wheels for the first time, into the ground-test area adjacent to the main assembly hall.

More orders

While all this engineering activity was under way, the sales people had released details of three additional orders. In March 1961 Lufthansa became the third customer overall and the first from overseas, when it ordered 12 aircraft for its growing network of European inter-city services. American Airlines — despite its earlier misgivings about the 727 — had obviously taken a long, hard look at its competitive situation *vis-a-vis* United and Eastern, and on 16 May signed a letter of intent for 25 aircraft: this letter was subsequently converted into a firm contract on 10 August 1961, which gave Boeing three out of the four big domestic carriers, totalling

105 aircraft between them. Trans World Airlines (the last of the big four) was initially a major disappointment, because in September 1961 it announced that its choice of short-range jet would be an 'Americanised' version of the French Caravelle, powered by General Electric CJ805-23C aft-fan engines: 25 of these aircraft had already been ordered, and another 15 put on option. This decision seemed reasonably final to Boeing, and it terminated all hopes of an order for 727s — until, that is, the airline ran short of money. A massive cash crisis affected not only the Caravelle purchase, but also an ambitious order for 26 additional 707s, which had been negotiated with Seattle in August 1961. When the airline later approached Boeing to ask for more time to pay (both for the aircraft and for their separately-contracted Pratt & Whitney engines), an imaginative financial package was put together by the two creditor companies. This involved a small overall reduction in the 707 order, and then a part-purchase/part-leasing arrangement for the remaining aircraft and engines: as an integral part of the deal, the paymasters agreed to include the financing of 10 Pratt & Whitney-powered Boeing 727s, with deliveries commencing in April 1964. Although the aircraft was not an ideal choice for TWA at that time, the single-source financial arrangement was irresistible: the Caravelle order was cancelled, and in March 1962 Boeing became the first manufacturer to sell a single type to all four of the major domestic carriers.

Below:
With its first order announced on roll-out day, Ansett-ANA was among the first group of 727 operators.
Gordon Reid

Roll-out

After leaving the assembly hall, the first 727 temporarily became the 'property' of scores of test engineers, who were given less than a month to prepare the aircraft, first for its publicity-seeking roll-out ceremony, and then for the much more serious business of working-up towards the start of flight testing. For roll-out the aircraft simply had to be painted (no easy task on that scale) and 'prettied-up' for the delight of several thousand guests, but before any flying could be done, nearly 16,000lb of test instrumentation had to be installed, together with a series of pumps and inter-connected water tanks that would enable the aircraft's centre-of-gravity to be changed in flight. All of this equipment had to be exhaustively tested using three early JT8Ds, before flight-approved engines arrived from East Hartford. Back in the production area, major sections of three more 727s were easily recognisable, with the second airframe already approaching structural completion.

The roll-out ceremony on 27 November 1962 was not the glitzy affair that modern marketing men would have wanted. No disco music or dazzling light-show, no swirling pools of vapour from truck-loads of dry-ice — instead, guests from many actual or potential customers happily mingled with representatives from all the major suppliers and even staff from the factory. After the briefest of speeches from Boeing executives, the hangar doors opened and the aircraft (N7001U, by now decked-out in the familiar chocolate and cream company colours but ultimately destined for United Airlines), was towed into the chill Seattle air. Perhaps the best

news of the day — certainly as far as the factory employees were concerned — was the confirmation that morning of two additional customers. Ansett–ANA and the state-owned Trans Australian Airlines each wanted two aircraft, bringing the total up to 131 orders from seven different airlines.

Preparing for flight

The first three production-standard JT8D-1 engines were delivered to Renton in early January, which allowed all the pre-flight clearances to be stepped-up a gear. Most of the tests done with the earlier development engines had to be repeated, but at least the production units were identical to each other, and the systems readings could be properly compared. The crew selected for the first flight were: S. L. 'Lew' Wallick, Boeing senior experimental test pilot and 727 project pilot (captain); R. L. 'Dix' Loesch, Boeing chief of flight test (co-pilot); and M. K. Shulenberger, Boeing chief flight engineer. These three men began to spend an increasing amount of their time in and around the new 'prototype', conducting most of the engine trials themselves, and eventually moving the aircraft under its own power for the first time towards the end of January.

The taxying trials were conducted in several distinct phases, beginning with straightforward rolling, turning and stopping at ground-idle power settings. These simple manoeuvres quickly developed into full ground-handling trials, which established most of the low-speed steering and braking limitations. The aircraft then went onto the runway for the first time to conduct a long series of accelerate/stop tests, each one reaching a progressively higher energy level. The efficiency of mechanical braking was compared with various reverse-thrust settings, and all the timings and forces were recorded for later analysis. The final sequence of accelerations pushed the aircraft right up to — and in some cases just beyond — its natural take-off speed, which provided good working values for V^r (rotation) and V^1 (lift-off), and allowed both pilots to feel the onset of aerodynamic control forces: during some of these later runs, the aircraft was 'floated' just a few feet off the runway for several seconds.

After 10 days of punishing ground trials, the 727 was returned to the workshops for a comprehensive inspection and rectification programme, which included the pre-planned replacement of all six tyres and much of the overworked braking system. This done, Lew Wallick had the aircraft signed over to him at first-light on Saturday, 9 February 1963, and immediately asked for 5,500 US gal of fuel to be pumped aboard. He and his crew meanwhile, together with a hand-picked group of project technicians, began the detailed task of clearing the machine for its first flight. A number of special check-lists had been prepared, involving not only the organic systems on the aircraft itself, but also most of the test equipment and its associated recording and telemetry units: everything had to be working properly, because no observers would be carried during the critical first few hours of flying.

Airborne at last

The three engines were started sequentially at about 10.45hr, and after a quick round of power-on systems checks, the ground-based technicians disembarked, leaving the flight crew to attend to their own cockpit drills. As soon as he was happy with the aircraft, Wallick eased gently forward for a final brake test, and then taxied away from the ramp area just after 11.00hr. Hundreds of factory workers from the joint 707/727 assembly line turned out to watch the aircraft as it stopped briefly on the holding area to stabilise powerplant temperatures and pressures, before moving onto the runway to complete its pre-take-off thrust checks and await clearance from the tower.

Brake release for the first flight was officially timed at 11.33hr. The aircraft accelerated rapidly towards its anticipated rotation speed of 119kt, and lift-off at 130,000lb was achieved just beyond the 3,000ft marker. For the first few minutes Wallick simply held the 727 in a 15° dead-ahead climb, keeping the wings level and the configuration unchanged until he reached a safe stall-recovery altitude. An initial handling assessment was completed during the first hour, leaving more than enough time to explore some of the low-speed end of the performance range before attempting a landing. Several times, the speed was reduced until the onset of pre-stall buffeting — both in 'clean' condition, and then with various leading-edge and flap settings. This gave the crew a clear idea of what to expect in the way of control responses, before a number of complete landing approaches were simulated at safe altitude. The first actual landing was done at Paine Field, near Everett (about 30 miles north of Seattle), where the aircraft was due to be based for its initial 10hr programme of FAA general air-worthiness flying. Touchdown was timed at 13.32hr, and the stopping distance on the runway was recorded at just over 2,000ft.

In general terms, the first flight had gone extremely well, and the crew was typically fulsome in its praise for the 727 — with Lew Wallick, in particular, being quoted as saying that the aircraft 'behaved better than expected in many respects'. This carefully chosen accolade was probably true at the time, but chief project engineer Jack Steiner knew (and later revealed at a meeting of aeronautical engineers) that everything had not gone entirely to plan: the centre engine had surged immediately after rotation, and then recovered to provide normal power for the rest of the flight. In the hubbub of celebration, the transitory surge must have seemed quite unimportant — a freak event that could have happened to any aircraft — but when the same thing happened on several later flights, the design team realised it was something rather more serious. Tracing the precise cause of the flow-separation proved to be incredibly difficult. All the conventional methods of investigating the problem failed to come up with an answer, so the entire S-duct was 'tufted' to highlight the moment of breakaway, and live pictures were transmitted to a closed-circuit TV monitor in the aircraft's cabin. The problem was greatly reduced by changes to the internal profile of the duct, but the No 2 engine has never achieved a spotless record on the 727. Surges on rotation still occur from time to time, but they are now considered to be rare events, and the powerplant generally recovers without any intervention from the crew.

Test programme

The overall flight-test and certification programme for the 727 was based at Boeing Field (the old King County Municipal Airport), two miles southwest of the Seattle city limits and just across the lake from Renton: in addition, some of the more specialised flying was conducted from Edwards AFB in California; Albuquerque in New Mexico and Denver, Colorado. The second aircraft (N72700 – destined to spend all its life as the company demonstrator) flew for the first time on 12 March and immediately joined N7001U, which had just returned to the Flight Test Center after its mandatory excursion to Paine Field. These two machines bore the brunt of the technical and scientific flying, with 430hr of structural damping and flutter tests allocated to No 1, and 320hr of systems development to No 2: each aircraft was individually instrumented for its assigned task, and every flight was carefully planned to ensure sequential clearances right up to certification. The original aircraft had to work through the entire speed range (up to Mach 0.95) with every conceivable combination of standard and non-standard fuel loading, while the second — with its heavy concentration on proving the electrical, hydraulic and braking systems — tended to lean more towards the lower end of the speed scale.

The third aircraft (N7002U for United) flew on 10 April 1963, and eventually completed most of the detailed handling and aerodynamic-loading trials. Its allocated programme of 180hr seemed relatively light in comparison with the others, but the flying itself was exceptionally arduous, involving extreme out-of-trim conditions, and often including semi-aerobatic manoeuvres such as rapid pull-ups, side-slips and even barrel rolls. This punishing regime was essential to establish the safe operating limits of the new airliner, and much of the feedback went straight into the preparation of training documentation and flight-manuals.

The fourth and last test aircraft was N68650, which was originally ordered by United as N7003U, but later re-allocated by Boeing (with United's approval) for temporary attachment to the Japanese carrier, All Nippon. This aircraft flew for the first time on 22 May, and was more or less fully furnished right from the start. Its primary task was a 313hr programme of proving passenger amenities such as pressurisation, air-conditioning and soundproofing, but it was also used for demonstrations to potential customers, and in its first six months completed a long sales tour which took it many thousands of miles away from the comforts of Boeing Field.

At the beginning of the programme, staff at the Test Center estimated that full certification of the 727 would absorb 1,243hr of flying. Of these, 320 were devoted to aerodynamic development; 60 to flutter tests; 145 to the powerplants and fuel system; and 50 to a thorough structural assessment. The formal process of certification (flying with FAA pilots and inspectors on board) would take 541hr, leaving just 127hr for 'in-house' development and testing, and for subsidiary tasks such as noise measurement. Additional hours also had to be found from somewhere for vital sales demonstrations.

Static testing

While the certification trials were under way, the first of two non-flying airframes was tested to destruction in a rig capable of applying static loads far in excess of the maximum expected in normal service. These tests confirmed that the aircraft was strong enough to take not only its

basic design loads, but also the generous safety margins built into the materials specification. That done, the tests continued way beyond the point of 'reasonable' behaviour, with pressure increasing until minor parts of the structure began to buckle, and finally the major load-bearing members suffered catastrophic failure. Careful monitoring of these tests gave the engineers a clear idea of where — and under what ultimate load — various elements of the structure were likely to break.

The imposition of static loads was essential to prove the overall integrity of the structure, but one-off stresses could not predict the wearying effect of years of passenger flying. To do this, a second ground-test specimen was installed in a hydraulically-activated, dynamic fatigue rig. Starting in April 1963, this particular airframe was repeatedly loaded and unloaded to simulate all the twists and distortions encountered during the daily grind of airline life. The hydraulics were pre-programmed to reproduce complete cycles of take-off, pressurisation, random manoeuvres, gust loads, depressurisation and the impact of landing. Each 'flight' was condensed into its basic stress-inducing elements, so a one-hour programme was equal to about 8hr of normal day-to-day service. None of the individual forces involved were quite as spectacular as those used in the static rig, but the regular application of realistic flight loads allowed the whole structure to 'age' in a much more controlled fashion. The initial design life of the 727 was 60,000hr over a 20-year period of operation, but the rig was run almost continuously for nearly 16 months, and eventually accumulated more than 90,000hr without any major problem.

Better than predicted

Despite the potentially difficult combination of a new airframe and untried engines, the flight testing of the 727 made excellent progress: there were few mechanical delays, and the four trials aircraft quickly proved themselves to be far better in many respects than Boeing expected them to be. Measured drag was a good deal lower than predicted, and this allowed the recommended cruising speed to be increased by 10kt while the average fuel consumption fell by about 5.5%. Familiarity with the JT8D-1 engines greatly enhanced their serviceability and operational efficiency, and Pratt & Whitney soon felt confident enough to offer customers a 2.5% improvement in their earlier specific fuel consumption guarantees — this over and above the savings already made possible by the

Left:
The busy Flight Test Centre at Boeing Fields handles everything from early 'prototype' trials to post-production clearance flights. The picture (taken at the end of April 1979) shows pre-delivery examples of the 737, the long-bodied 727-200, the conventional 747-200 and the long-range 747-SP.

Above:
After its initial success with the 727-100, Lufthansa was an obvious customer for the much bigger 200-series. D-ABKT was delivered in January 1979, but was ultimately replaced — along with all the other 727s — by a fleet of Airbus A300s. *Hugh Newell*

airframe drag performance. The aircraft could also be flown much more slowly than expected on approach, and its runway-braking capabilities — particularly at heavy landing weights — were far better than originally promised.

Although the trials began much later than planned, the exceptional reliability of the aircraft allowed the Test Center to claw back most of the lost time fairly quickly, and by the end of June 1963, the programme was more or less back on schedule for December certification. Two additional aircraft (N7004U and N7005U — both destined for United) flew in June, and these were followed in July and August by another pair for United and N8101N, the first in the colours of Eastern Airlines. These five were all standard production machines, and although they took no part in the formal certification programme, they were used extensively for airline-crew familiarisation rides, and to train the initial cadre of airline instructors.

After completion of the basic in-house development flying, certification-proper got under way in mid-July. By that time, the lead aircraft (N7001U) had accumulated more than 250hr in the air, averaging a remarkable 27hr per week since its first flight in February. During their 500hr validation programme, FAA pilots and inspectors handled the aircraft through every conceivable systems and instrument failure. Stalls and general manoeuvres were conducted way outside the recommended weight and centre-of-gravity limits, and a series of overload take-offs eventually achieved a maximum rotation weight of 160,000lb. The upper end of the speed range was explored to within a few percentage points of Mach 1.0, and high-energy landings were made using less than 1,000ft of runway to bring the heavy aircraft to a complete stop. Single and multiple engine shut-downs and re-lights were examined in several combinations and situations, with special attention being given to the worst-case possibilities of losing power on rotation or having to cope with asymmetric thrust-reversers on a slippery surface. Later in the programme (following the crash in England of the T-tailed BAC One-Eleven prototype) the stalling characteristics were investigated in much greater detail, and angles-of-attack in excess of 50° were flown in order to confirm the effectiveness of both the powered elevator system and its manual back-up.

Sales tour

By the end of August 1963, enough progress had been made in the certification trials to allow the FAA to issue a Provisional Type Certificate. This document was not an authorisation for revenue-earning passenger flights, but it did release the first few aircraft for restricted crew-training duties, and it also cleared the fourth (fully furnished) test aircraft to embark on an ambitious sales demonstration tour.

Many people in Seattle thought it was crazy to

plan such a long tour only seven months after the first 727 had flown, but overseas airlines needed to see the aircraft before making any commitments, and overall despatch reliability had been so good during the preceding test programme that the company did not expect to run into any major problems. Confidence was so high at that stage that no spares or special tools were sent on ahead, and the use of a separate support aircraft was never seriously considered. Instead, everything needed for the trip was carried on board, and 15-20 service engineers accompanied the aircraft to provide round-the-clock maintenance cover.

The first phase of the tour began on 25 August, with a relatively simple route around 14 cities in the United States and Canada. These sectors covered a total distance of about 8,500 miles, but the aircraft was never more than a few hours flying time away from Boeing Field, and instant contact between the tour party and the Flight Test Center could virtually be guaranteed. The real adventure started on 17 September, when the aircraft took-off from Montreal, bound for the Azores on the first leg of a six-week overseas journey. These were the days before satellite communications had been established, and everyone on board was aware of the risk that they might be out of touch for several days at a time — frustrated, perhaps, by a combination of changing time-zones, different languages, and the problems of using land-line telephone systems routed through various under-developed countries.

After refuelling on the Azores and night-stopping in Rome, the aircraft continued broadly southeast and flew demonstrations in Beirut, Karachi, Calcutta, Bangkok and Manila, before arriving in Tokyo for one of the major objectives of the tour — a week-long proving trial over some of the domestic route network of both Japan Airlines and All Nippon. Under Government pressure, these two carriers had already agreed to buy the same type of short/medium range jet, and Boeing was involved in an uncompromising battle for the orders, in direct competition with Britain's de Havilland Trident (which was also on tour at that time, and scheduled to arrive in Tokyo about 10 days after the 727's departure).

Following what appeared to be a highly successful visit to Japan, the Boeing team continued on towards Darwin, Sydney and Melbourne, where they introduced the 727 to local airport authorities, and arranged courtesy flights for the Australian travel industry and regional press. This phase of the tour was partially sponsored by existing customers TAA and Ansett, which allowed both of them to gain limited experience of handling the aircraft before their own were delivered, starting in September 1964.

After nearly a week devoted mostly to public relations work, the demonstrator resumed its quest for sales with visits to Singapore, Calcutta, Bombay, Karachi (where it briefly shared the airfield with the Tokyo-bound Trident) and Baghdad, before arriving in Africa for presentations at Khartoum, Nairobi and Johannesburg. By mid-October the whole team was heading north again — this time bound for Athens and the start of a busy European tour, which included planned stopovers in Rome, Zurich, Paris, Brussels and Amsterdam. Several days were then spent with Lufthansa (the first overseas buyer) at Frankfurt and Hamburg, and a final demonstration was arranged in Stockholm before the aircraft was fuelled-up and made ready for its long journey home.

Having amazed everyone within its near-perfect reliability, the aircraft returned to Seattle in considerable triumph on 31 October, after visiting 26 countries (including fuel stops) in just seven weeks. The tour party had covered a nominal distance of 94,483 miles in an elapsed flight time of 194hr 16min, which gave a remarkable average over short stage lengths of 486mph. Presentations were made to nearly 40 airlines, and 139 separate departures had been achieved without a single mechanical delay. The only significant maintenance work undertaken during the tour were the replacements of one main-gear brake unit; two booster pumps from the fuel system; a pitch-change motor in the tailplane, and five tyres. The JT8D-1 powerplants behaved flawlessly throughout, as did the cabin systems, which were still very much under test while the tour was in progress.

The aircraft itself (N68650) was given a thorough post-tour inspection at the Flight Test Center, and then went on to complete its allocated share of the certification flying. In mid-January 1964, the two Japanese airlines at last justified all the expense and difficulty of the tour, by announcing their intention to buy 727s instead of the rival Trident. As part of the deal, the demonstrator was brought up to full passenger-carrying standard and flown back to the Far East for a year — leased by All Nippon to train crews and establish a regular Tokyo/Sapporo service in advance of their own deliveries. After returning from Japan (and still carrying its US registration) the aircraft played a similar role in the Iran Air purchase of 727s during 1965-66, and was actually out on lease again (this time to North Carolina-based Piedmont Airlines), when it was destroyed in a mid-air collision on 19 July 1967.

Certification

The full passenger-carrying Certificate of Airworthiness was issued by the FAA on 20 December 1963. At its initial gross weight of 142,000lb, the basic aircraft was cleared to operate from 5,500ft runways at sea-level in standard (ISA) conditions, or from a 6,600ft strip at ISA + 5°c. Within these limits, the design-maximum payload of 24,000lb could be carried with enough fuel on board for a single stage-length of about 1,000 miles (depending on cruise conditions). With full tanks (7,000 US gal) the range could almost be doubled, but the payload on departure would be limited by fuel-weight to about 12,000lb. An optional, longer-range version of the aircraft, was offered with an additional 500 US gal of fuel housed in a bag-tank in the wing/fuselage centre-section: this was cleared for take-off at 152,000lb, but its field length requirements for ISA and ISA + 5° were 6,300ft and 8,200ft respectively. Both versions were ultimately cleared for take-off at up to 160,000lb, but this level of performance was only achieved by using reduced flap settings on a much longer runway. The maximum landing weight of the standard airframe was structurally limited to 131,000lb, but some of the early United Airlines models were strengthened to allow landings at up to 135,000lb.

The approved passenger capacity was determined by the size, location and efficiency of the emergency exits. In its original form the aircraft had two large doors ahead of the wing (the forward cabin and starboard galley doors); one Type III and one Type IV overwing exit on each side of the fuselage (both types 20in by 38in, but the rear pair were classified differently because of the step down onto the wing); and the main entrance to the aft cabin, which was centrally located under the tail. This basic arrangement would normally allow a peak capacity of 114 passengers, but the FAA approved 119 for the 727, because both forward doors were fitted with inflatable escape slides. The rear entrance was not included in the first set of escape proposals, because it lacked a simple emergency system for opening the bulkhead door and lowering the integral stairs. Once this had been rectified by Boeing, the FAA accepted the ventral door as a reliable means of escape, and the modified aircraft were cleared to carry a maximum of 131.

Deliveries

The first few deliveries were made to the two launch customers in the late autumn of 1963 — but at that early stage the aircraft could only be operated under the restrictive terms of the Provisional Type Certificate. United Airlines accepted the first (N7004U) on 29 October, and Eastern took the second (N8102N) on 15 November. These were followed in late November by N7006U and N7005U (both for United), and then one more for each airline during the run-up to the Christmas break (N8103N for Eastern and N7007U for United). These six aircraft formed the nucleus of a busy 727 training programme, with each carrier using staff instructors schooled by Boeing, to prepare their own air and ground crews for the start of passenger services.

More than 20 727s had flown by the certification date in December, and the production rate was already creeping up towards the five per month mark. New aircraft seen in and around the Flight Test Center over Christmas included five more for Eastern, four for United, and the first two (N1971 and N1972) destined for American Airlines. Across the lake at Renton several more — including a third for American and the first (D-ABIB) for Lufthansa — were structurally complete, and either in the paint shop or undergoing their final pre-flight checks. Behind them, on the factory floor, the joint 707/720/727 assembly line was gradually being accelerated to produce at least eight tri-jets every month by the end of 1964.

The delivery of 'stockpiled' aircraft was stepped-up immediately after certification, and by the end of the first quarter of 1964 Eastern and United were both operating 10 of their initial batches of 40. American Airlines and Lufthansa also took their first few deliveries during this period, and in late April Trans World Airlines and All Nippon Airways became the fifth and sixth operators (albeit, in ANA's case, with only the leased demonstrator). By the end of the year no fewer than 101 aircraft had been delivered to 10 separate airlines.

Into service

The 727 finally began earning money for its customers on 1 February 1964, when an Eastern Airlines aircraft fitted with 28 first and 66 tourist-class seats took-off to replace the regular

Above:
Sabena operated five short-bodied 727-100s (including three Convertible passenger/cargo models) during the late 1960s, but the fleet was never upgraded to the higher-capacity of the 200-series. Instead, the Belgian carrier switched all its short-range traffic onto the twin-engined 737, and the tri-jets were disposed-of after less than 10 years service. *Sabena*

Below:
Seen here at Tempelhof Airport in Berlin, N325PA was among the first batch of 727-100s delivered to Pan Am. They were originally ordered in 1965, and subsequently used to replace DC-6Bs on the airline's internal German services. *Peter Gilchrist*

Lockheed Electra on a Miami-Washington-Philadelphia service. United Airlines followed-on just five days later, when it introduced the aircraft on the San Francisco-Denver route. Both flights had come less than a year after the first 727 had taken-off from Renton — which was a remarkable achievement in any terms, but especially significant compared with the 27 months that elapsed between the first flight and the first service of the rival Trident.

The basic engineering of the 727 is more than 30 years old now, but the remarkable strength designed into the airframe has lasted exceptionally well, and it seems increasingly certain that hundreds of the aircraft will remain in service way beyond the turn of the century. The tri-jet drew heavily on Boeing's late-1950s experience with the four-engined 707, and many components, internal systems and manufacturing techniques are common to both types. It would be wrong, however, to imagine that the 727 is simply a reworked 707, because the structural demands of any short-range aircraft are infinitely more complex than those of its longer-range cousins.

Torsion Box

The key to the long-term success of the 727 has undoubtedly been its amazingly tough wing. This was built-up from two plate-web and extruded-boom main spars supported by a large number of press-stiffened and perforated light-alloy ribs. The basic fail-safe framework was transformed into a full torsion-box with the addition of upper and lower skin panels, which extend from root-attachment points on the fuselage virtually out to the tip. The upper panel was machined from a

single plank of zinc-based 7178ST aluminium alloy, continuously tapered both across the chord and along the span to produce maximum thicknesses of 0.75in inboard and just 0.060in near the tip; after its final profiling operation, the panel was stiffened by constant-section rolled-aluminium stringers, which were attached

Below:
This picture clearly shows some of the features of the brilliant 727 wing design. The low-speed (outer) and high-speed (inner) ailerons are visible as dark patches on the trailing-edge, and the colour change across 95% of the full span shows the position of the rear spar. The forward spar is not so apparent, but it extends conventionally from root to tip, and joins the fuselage just ahead of the two emergency exits. The darker skin panelling between the spars bears considerable flight loads, and is milled from solid planks of 7178ST aluminium alloy, varying in thickness from 0.75in at the root to 0.060in near the tip. The lighter material aft of the torsion-box consists almost exclusively of much thinner, non-load-bearing aluminium honeycomb. This area includes very little fixed wing skin, because most of the surface aft of the torsion-box can be moved in some way — either as trailing-edge flaps, or as separate spoiler groups designed for ground and flight use. The very light area close to the wing root is not a structural feature, but a non-slip escape path to guide passengers over the trailing-edge.

separately rather than being machined from the solid. The lower skin was prepared and stiffened in much the same way, but because flight loads under the wing are predominantly tensile (rather than compressive), three spanwise planks of copper-based 2024ST were chosen, instead of the single billet of 7178. More than 20 inspection hatches (one for each major rib space) were machined into the centre plank, and the whole box was sealed to carry fuel.

The port and starboard sides were completed as separate sub-assemblies, before being joined together at either end of an unswept centre-section box. The full-span wing was then installed on special shop-floor jigs, while the rear fuselage and tail assembly (already combined as a single production unit at that stage) were lowered into position and attached with multiple taper-lock bolts.

Centre Section

The primary flight and landing loads on the 727 structure are carried through and around the fuselage on three very large, forged and machined, light-alloy ring frames — two of which link directly to the front and rear wing spars, while the third is indirectly attached to the swept-back face of the rear spar by a heavy, forged-alloy, undercarriage support beam. These frames correspond with structural stations 740, 870 and 950 (inches from the forward pressure bulkhead). The passenger-deck flooring between all three is specially reinforced to contain the cabin pressure above, while the lower lobes of the two outer frames (740 and 950) are blanked-off with bulkhead-strength sheet webs — effectively creating a large, unpressurised compartment beneath the central cabin area.

The forward section of this underfloor compartment (between 740 and 870) is principally occupied by the wing carry-through structure, but many of the cabin air-conditioning elements (including the primary and secondary heat-exchangers, water-separators and cold-air units) are installed directly beneath the wing, protected from the outside airflow by a huge fibreglass fairing, wrapped around the wing/fuselage intersection. Aft of the wing box (between frames 870 and 950), the unpressurised area is divided fore-and-aft by a 63in deep vertical keel member. This was used by the structural engineers to stiffen the fuselage between the cavernous undercarriage bays, but it also carries various essential services (fuel, hydraulics, electrical cables and air-conditioning ducts, etc) across the 80in gap, and provides a convenient housing for the optional — though usually fitted — AiResearch GTC-85 auxiliary power unit (APU) and its associated 40kVA generator. The intake for the APU is hidden inside the wheel bay, and the turbine exhaust is ducted through the fuselage to emerge on the upper surface of the starboard wing, where its outlet is protected in flight by a hydraulically-operated flap. The two wheel bays also house power units for the ailerons and training-edge flap groups, and the lower edge of the keel supports the hinges and power-packages for the double-fold mainwheel doors.

Flying Controls

The flying-control layout of the 727 bears an obvious family resemblance to that of the 707, but the need for lower flying speeds has added a new level of sophistication to most of the moving surfaces. The 707 was equipped with a predominantly manual (control-tab) system, but the tri-jet was designed from the outset to have duplicated hydraulic circuits on all three axes, with automatic manual reversion in pitch and roll; a third, stand-by hydraulic system is also available, to supply emergency operating power to all leading-edge devices and part of the split-section rudder.

Lateral control in cruising flight is derived from a pair of short-span inboard ailerons, assisted by spoiler panels on the top surface of each wing. An additional pair of outboard (low-speed) ailerons remain centrally locked during the cruise, but as soon as the trailing-edge flap groups move away from their stowed position, a clever mechanical linkage disengages the drive to all flight spoilers, and transfers their supplementary roll authority to the outboard ailerons. A similar (but reverse) sequence occurs during take-off, with the low-speed ailerons remaining in the control-loop until the retracting flaps automatically activate the spoiler system. The switch from spoilers to ailerons and back again prevents airflow breakaway over the complex flap system, and lengthens the vital control arm while the aircraft is flying at low speeds and high angles-of-attack.

Spoilers

Each wing has seven spoiler panels hinged to its top surface — three set close to the fuselage, and a separate group of four positioned between the inboard and outboard ailerons. The two panels on each side closest to the passenger cabin (four in all) are used only on the ground. These are mechanically locked by retraction of

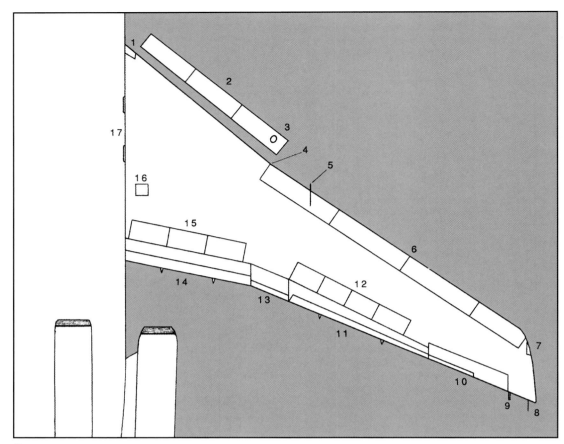

Key:
1   Fixed landing lamp in wing root
2   Three rigid Kreuger sections (these extend down and forwards from hinges set into the underside of the leading edge)
3   Retractable landing lamp mounted on the outboard Kreuger section
4   Kinked leading-edge
5   Small wing fence mounted on the inboard slat section
6   Four sections of leading edge-slat
7   Navigation lamp
8   Static discharge wick
9   Fuel jettison pipe
10 Outer (low-speed) aileron with manual-reversion tab
11 Outer triple-slotted flap group
12 Four outboard spoiler panels (used with one section of the inboard group, for in-flight lift dumping and supplementary roll control; also for lift-dumping on the ground)
13 Inner (all-speeds) aileron with manual-reversion tab
14 Inner triple-slotted flap group
15 Inboard spoiler panels (two closest to fuselage used only for lift dumping on the ground, outer one used as part of 12 above)
16 Auxiliary power unit (APU) exhaust flap
17 Overwing emergency exits (two each side)

the main undercarriage, and are preset to deploy to their full 45° when oleo compression is sensed on landing; they then act solely as lift dumpers, scrubbing off speed and forcing the aircraft to settle firmly on the runway. The remaining 10 spoilers (both outer groups and one from each inner group) are multi-function devices, operable in separate roll-assist, air-brake and lift-dumper modes. These are all connected to the pilots' control wheels by duplicated push-pull cables, routed through a powered rate-cam in each side of the lower fuselage. The cables operate single-source hydraulic rams at each spoiler position, and in the roll-assist mode the port and starboard panels are raised differentially to add power to the downgoing wing. For air-braking, all 10 panels can be raised in unison with a single cockpit lever, giving any deflection angle up to a maximum of 40°. This powerful system can provide high-altitude let-down rates in excess of 6,000ft/min if necessary, enabling the aircraft to plunge steeply into a busy terminal area with the minimum of fuss; during the descent, normal

Seen on the final loop of the assembly area, these Advanced 727-200s are only days away from completion. In this 'green' state, various protective finishes help to show some of the sub-assemblies that come together to make up a complete aircraft. The fuselage panelling stands out particularly well, as does the lighter colour of the wing torsion-box. Most of the aircraft here have their spoiler groups and leading-edge devices deployed to some degree, but only one (closest to the camera) has its engines fitted. The outwards-opening, underfloor cargo-hold doors of the 200-series are noticeable (the equivalent 100-series doors open inwards), and minor changes to the customer-specification — such as window layout aft of the rear emergency exit and different radome materials — are just about visible. At this point in mid-1977, the line was turning out at least seven aircraft every month.

roll-control functions can be maintained by superimposing differential spoiler commands on to the chosen brake setting. When the trailing-edge flaps are used during the early stages of final approach, all 10 flight spoilers return to their parked position on the wing, and from there, they can be pre-armed or deployed manually to act as additional lift-dumpers on touchdown.

Flaps

The advanced trailing-edge flaps on the 727 are triple-slotted to provide the best available coefficient of lift at low flying speeds — but they open-out into three separate components only near the end of their permitted travel. This deployment geometry ensures that the low-drag, area-increasing benefits of a Fowler-type flap are retained for as long as possible, which helps to provide a wide range of take-off settings and ensures a smooth deceleration during the early stage of final approach. The flap carriages are mounted on the central (main) flap of each group; they operate on machined steel tracks which originate almost horizontally under the wing, before turning downwards well clear of the fixed structure. This track shape allows considerable rearwards travel of the flap, before the whole assembly reaches the curve and begins to rotate — still basically in one aerodynamic piece. As the curve is negotiated,

pawls on each track arrest the movement of the fore-flap and pull it clear, while the main flap continues its downward path under the influence of two rotating screwjacks; as the fore-flap is arrested, a pair of cables attached to its trailing edge begin to turn two small pulleys inside the body of the main flap, and push-rod cranks attached to these finally deploy the small aft-flap. The operating rails for the fore-flap and aft-flap are integral parts of the driven main-flap, and the ingenious deployment sequence is common to both inner and outer flap groups.

The primary flap actuator system is split into two, with the inboard and outboard groups being driven separately by an identical pair of fuselage-mounted hydraulic motors. The rotary

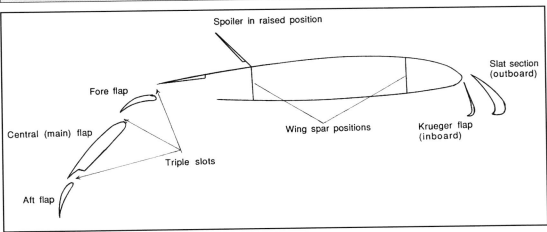

Spoiler in raised position

Slat section (outboard)

Fore flap

Wing spar positions

Krueger flap (inboard)

Central (main) flap

Triple slots

Aft flap

output for each individual group is carried via torque-tubes to four long screwjacks — one at each end of both the major flap sections. The two hydraulic motors are situated in the mainwheel bays, and each has a co-located electric motor to provide stand-by power. All the flaps (both groups) are signalled by one cockpit lever, which is gated to provide 2°, 5°, 15°, 25°, 30°, and 40° settings; gate 'locks' are incorporated in the 5° and 25° positions to prevent inadvertent selection of full flap with one sweep of the handle. Flap travel is monitored in the cockpit by a pair of twin-needled flap position indicators, which quickly highlight any

asymmetry between the port and starboard sections of either group; if any mismatch exceeds 7°, further rearwards travel of the offending pair is inhibited, while the other pair continues to operate normally.

Leading-edge devices

The high-lift devices on the forward part of each wing consist of three sections of Krueger flap inboard of the leading-edge kink, and four slat sections outboard; each system is used for both take-off and landing, and their deployment sequences are largely automatic. The slats begin to appear whenever the trailing-edge flaps are

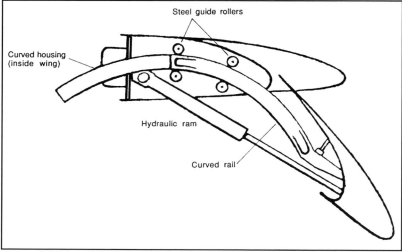

Above:
With its full-span leading-edge devices and 20° of flap deployed, this Royal New Zealand AF 727-100 demonstrates a typical take-off configuration.
Hugh Newell

Left:
The 727's slat deployment system has recently been revived and incorporated on the high-tech 777.

Below left:
The Krueger panels fold inwards to form part of the underside of the wing leading edge.

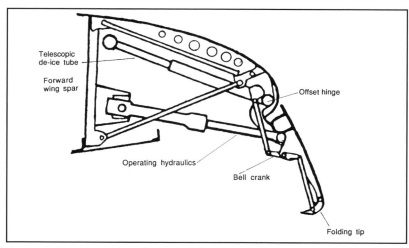

selected. Two degrees of flap (which generates much rearwards travel but very little deflection) brings the centre pair of slats on each side into operation, and 5° of flap triggers the remaining slat pairs and all six Kruegers. In each case the sections are hydraulically deployed either fully-open or fully-closed; there are no intermediate settings.

The slat sections are built as miniature aerofoils in their own right, with sheet-alloy skins, light internal ribbing and a reinforced leading-edge to resist rain and hail erosion. Accurate positioning over the full limit of their travel is determined by a pair of curved rails, which are rigidly attached to the rear of each moving surface; these emerge from identically curved housings in the fixed wing structure, and move forwards and downwards between two sets of steel guide rollers. The Kruegers are manufactured as flat magnesium castings, which normally form part of the underskin of the leading-edge. Each section is mounted on three cabinet-style offset hinges, which allow the actual hinge-line to rotate down and around the forward lip of the wing while the panel is still in motion; the deployment sequence is completed by a neat bell-crank linkage, which unfolds and finally positions the rounded lower lip. Each slat and Krueger section is individually de-iced by hot air bled from the compressor stages of all three engines. The hot air is initially delivered to a fixed 'gas-main' system in the leading-edge of the wing, and then to each moving surface via a series of swivel-mounted, telescopic branch pipes; used (but still warm) air is vented back across the upper surface of the wing, which also

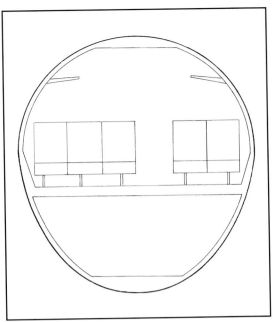

keeps that area clear and prevents ice being ingested into the engines.

Fuselage construction

The 727 fuselage betrays its 707 ancestry from almost every angle, but the two aircraft are distinctly different in engineering terms, and very little of one could be built in the jigs of the other. The full diameter of the 727 passenger cabin has exactly the same 148in external and 144in internal dimensions as that of the 707, but the aircraft are not the same length, and the lower lobe of the 727 fuselage (below floor level) is a completely new design — much shallower overall, and purpose-built for its shorter-range task. The 727 is also unusual among passenger jets, in that the lower lobe of the rear fuselage is 10in deeper than everything forward of the wing.

For manufacturing purposes the whole body and tail of the 727 was divided into four major sections, each built-up from smaller sub-assemblies in its own production jig, before being brought together in the final assembly area at Renton. Production techniques used on the aircraft followed a familiar Boeing pattern, with rolled-alloy hooped frames between every window space; perforated I-section floor beams across every frame; and an external skin supported on the inside by hundreds of feet of constant-section, aluminium stringers. The load-deck flooring consisted mainly of spot-welded panels of corrugated aluminium sandwich, and the window frames were manufactured as individual light-alloy forgings, which were bolted

Top right:
The 727 cross-section is 10in deeper aft of the wing.
Below:
The 707 fuselage is identical to the 727 above floor level, but has a deeper cargo compartment.

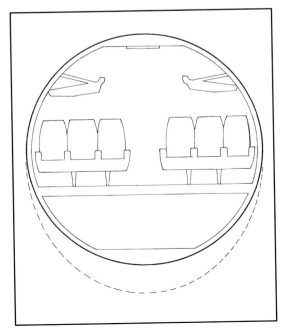

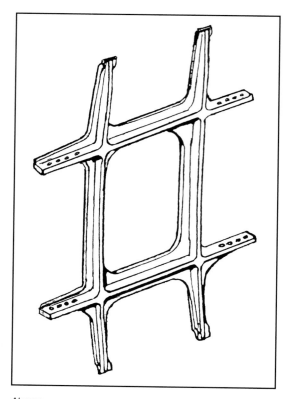

Above:
These light-alloy forgings surround each passenger-window on the 727.

the smallest of the four main production units. Virtually all skin panels in this section are double-curvature in some way, and most of the structure is identical to the same components on the 707. The weather radar (originally a Bendix RDR-1E X-band set, but probably by now on most aircraft) is mounted on the forward face of the bulkhead, and protected by an upwards-hingeing, glass-fibre nose cone. The flightdeck was designed for three operational crew members (pilot, co-pilot and flight-engineer), but it also carries a pair of supernumerary seats to accommodate the occasional aircrew-trainee, instructor or flight inspector. The equipment and instrumentation standards are broadly similar to those on the 707, but the centre console and flight-engineer's panel obviously reflect the three-engined layout and new systems configuration. Below floor level, space in the cockpit area is severely limited by the tapering profile of the nose; much of what is available is taken up by the forward end of the unpressurised nosewheel bay, but all the control runs and complex wiring harnesses are gathered together in this tiny compartment, and room still had to be found for two stick-shaker systems and the central-processing electronics for the Bendix radar. Maintenance access to all this equipment is only available via a small underside hatchway, located on the centreline and immediately aft of the forward bulkhead.

Section-43
The mid-fuselage section (Section-43) includes all the structure between the rear of Section-41 and the first of the big ring-frames at station 740. The upper lobe is entirely occupied by passenger services and accommodation, while separate areas below the floor house the rear end of the nosewheel bay; a roomy electronics and radio compartment; the first of two luggage and cargo holds; and a substantial part of the air-conditioning system. At its forward end, this section still forms part of the expanding, double-curvature profile of the nose, but the fuselage reaches its full external diameter immediately aft of the front passenger door, and thereafter all the skin panels are manufactured as single-curvature units. The 34in by 72in entrance door on the port side is identical to the outwards-opening, plug-type doors installed on the 707; an inflatable escape slide was fitted as standard on the 727, and electrically-operated air-stairs were offered as a customer option. A second, smaller door, is located on the starboard side of

together in series to form an immensely strong chain down each side of the cabin. Most of the window frames, emergency exits and passenger-door units were identical to those on the 707. The hooped fuselage frames (including the three main-frames in the centre) were made in several sections, which allowed single-curvature body panels to be assembled in small, easily-handled units; these were then joined together in main-production jigs, using pre-drilled frame sections and fork-ended stringers to locate each panel against its neighbour. Final fixings were predominantly aluminium rivets and steel bolts, with epoxy-resin bonding to reinforce rip-stopping doublers.

Section-41
On the factory floor the so-called forward fuselage (in effect, just the nose) was known as Section-41. This extends from the flat-plate pressure bulkhead 18in or so ahead of the windscreen apex, back to a circular frame just aft of the cockpit side windows. It included none of the full-diameter passenger cabin, and was

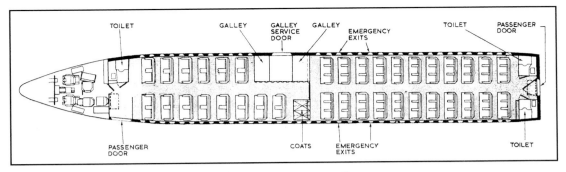

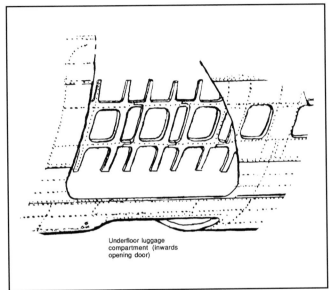

Underfloor luggage compartment (inwards opening door)

Above:
The short-fuselage 727-100 was typically configured with 28 first-class and 66 economy seats.

Left:
The side of the fuselage is stiffened by the chain of window surrounds.

This takes the form of a reinforced alloy box, which links up with a similar cut-out at the rear of section-41. Running across the fuselage above this bay, is a container for the Webber telescopic air-stair unit (if fitted), which stows neatly in the restricted space under the cabin floor, and emerges from the pressure shell through a 44in by 16in inwards-opening door; the entire operating sequence is electrically powered. Immediately aft of the undercarriage, the specialised avionics compartment houses most of the essential radio and electronic equipment on front and rear double-deck racks; normal access for maintenance is gained from below (though a manhole-sized hatchway on the centreline), but a trap-door is also provided in the cabin floor to allow for in-flight emergencies. Aft of the avionics bay, the 390cu/ft luggage compartment is nearly 17ft long and occupies the full width and height of the underfloor area; the 35in by 40in starboard loading door opens inwards and upwards (on the 100-series aircraft), leaving a nominal sill height of 60in.

the fuselage, just ahead of the wing. This was designed primarily as a galley service door, but its 33in by 65in dimensions made it an obvious choice as an emergency evacuation point, and a second escape slide was incorporated as part of the standard specification. The galley itself is fairly small on the 727, and its position within the cabin is virtually tied to that of the service door. For this reason, most airlines use it as a natural cabin divider, with four-abreast (first-class) accommodation in the forward area, and six-abreast tourist-class seats to the rear. Numbers vary between carriers, but a typical mix for the whole aircraft would be 28 first and 66 tourist-class seats, with a large coat-storage area directly opposite the galley unit. The forward cabin has a single toilet and washroom facility, located on the the starboard side, next to the flightdeck partition.

Below floor level, the first seven or eight circular frames of Section-43 are divided at the bottom by the rear portion of the nosewheel bay.

Section-46
The main structural part of the fuselage (the pressure shell) holds a constant 148in wide and 158in deep cross-section until it meets the big main-frame at station 740. At that point the production unit changes to Section-46, and the overall depth of the fuselage increases to 168in. The resulting 'step-down' under the centre-section is covered by the big fibreglass

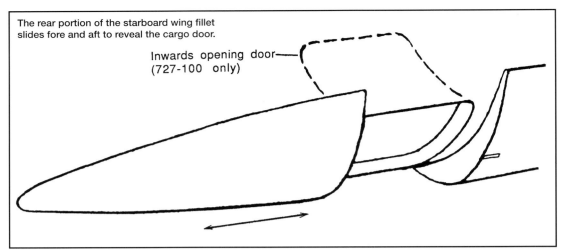

The rear portion of the starboard wing fillet slides fore and aft to reveal the cargo door.

Inwards opening door—(727-100 only)

honeycomb fairing, which extends rearwards to a position way beyond the wing. The extra 10in of lower-lobe depth — which was originally needed solely in the centre-section to accommodate the bulky air-conditioning plant and retracted main gear — was retained throughout the rear fuselage.

Section-46 encompasses everything from station 740 back to (and including) the pressure bulkhead at the rear of the passenger cabin. The upper lobe is basically an uncomplicated tube-like structure, with parallel sides over most of its length and evenly-spaced window units along both side-walls. There are no external doors in this part of the aircraft, but two conventional windows on each side have been replaced by 707-pattern (20in by 38in) overwing emergency exits. All three of the major ring-frames are incorporated in Section-46, and the bridging floor area between them is braced and

Right:
The 727-200s under construction at Renton illustrate several design features common to all models. The rear pressure-bulkhead is positioned directly beneath the thin, lighter-coloured 'horse-shoe' frame, which is looped over the centre-engine inlet cowl. This bulkhead is an immensely strong part of the structure, and is used to anchor the front spar of the fin box, and the Y-shaped forward mounting yokes for both side engines. On the underside of the fuselage, the tail-bumper loads are also diffused through the bulkhead frame. The centre engine (not yet fitted to the three aircraft closest to the camera) is hung horizontally under the fin, with its fan inlet positioned just to the rear of the visible firewall. All three engines are capable of breaking away without inflicting damage on the primary aircraft structure. At the top of the fin, the horizontal tail is a fully moving (trimmable) surface, with the elevator pivots extending directly from the rear face of its two-spar torsion box; the dual-circuit powered elevators are fitted with control-tabs (dark panels on the trailing-edge) to provide for manual reversion in the event of hydraulic failure. One of the aircraft here is undergoing final-assembly system tests, and is seen with its triple-slotted flaps fully extended and the spolier groups partially deployed.

reinforced to form an integral part of the pressure cabin. At the extreme rear of the section (between the two side engines) the fuselage begins to taper down towards the tail; the last three ring-frames, therefore, progressively diminish in size, and the exterior skin panels revert to a more complex three-dimensional shape. The flat-plate rear bulkhead is an enormously strong, double-skinned affair, stiffened both vertically and horizontally by a lattice of I-section beams, and incorporating a 32in by 76in plug-type passenger door which leads down to the ventral stairway. The toilet/washroom facilities for the rear cabin are installed against the bulkhead, with a single booth on either side of the central aisle. Throughout the aircraft, most of the passenger furnishings (seat units, side panels, window surrounds, etc) are fully interchangeable with those on a 707.

Below floor level, more than half of Section-46 is unpressurised — primarily to accommodate the central wing box and mainwheel bays, but the underwing area also houses most of the larger air-conditioning units. The bifurcated cold-air intake for the cabin air systems is actually located beneath the pressurised baggage hold at the rear of Section-43 — a long way forward of the units themselves. Ambient air is forced in under ram-pressure, and then ducted through the lower lobe bulkhead at station 740, into the unpressurised chamber immediately below the wing. There, it passes through the primary and secondary heat-exchangers, before being dumped overboard again through a quartet of outflow vents. Hot, compressor-bleed air for the system, is pre-cooled in the two side-engine struts, before being piped forwards into the

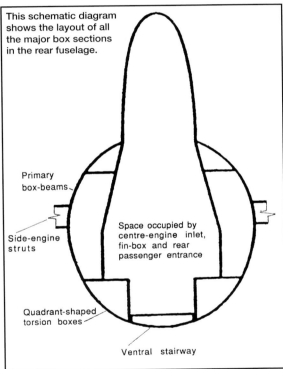

This schematic diagram shows the layout of all the major box sections in the rear fuselage.

Primary box-beams

Side-engine struts

Space occupied by centre-engine inlet, fin-box and rear passenger entrance

Quadrant-shaped torsion boxes

Ventral stairway

array of heat-exchangers, air-cycle machines and water separators; it then passes through the 740 bulkhead into the pressurised compartment, where all the mixing, distribution and control valves are located, in the 'snake-pit' beneath the floor of Section-43.

The pressurised underfloor area of Section-46 (aft of the mainwheel bays) is taken up solely by the 465cu/ft rear luggage compartment. This is similar in most respects to the forward hold, but its usable floor-to-ceiling height was increased

from 44in to 54in as a direct result of the deeper fuselage cross-section. The loading doors for both holds are identical, but easy access to the rear one was denied by the presence of the extended wing fillet (which is not, of course, part of the underlying pressure shell). To overcome this problem, Boeing mounted the tail end of the starboard fillet on 60in horizontal rails — similar to those used on the 707. The big moulding now unlocks from its normal flight position and slides aft to reveal the hidden door, which is then operated in the conventional way.

Above:
The split rudder sections and their big anti-balance tabs are clearly shown in this picture, as is the retractable 'bumper' which protects the centre engine in the event of an over-enthusiastic rotation. The screw-jack for tailplane trim-control is mounted vertically inside the fin, and located just aft of the leading-edge of the surface. *Peter Gilchrist*

Below:
The tall, sharply-swept fin of the 727 adds considerable elegance to the overall design, and relieves the slightly cluttered look associated with all rear-engined tri-jets.

Section-48

The tail section of the aircraft (Section-48) covers almost everything aft of the rear bulkhead — including the tail-fin, the ventral stairway, the side-engine pylons and the so-called S-duct leading down to the centre engine. The horizontal tail is a separate sub-assembly, but its pivot and operating mechanisms are effectively part of the fin. There are no windows in Section-48, and the whole internal volume is unpressurised. The primary fuselage structure

consists of two heavy-gauge, tapered box-beams, cantilevered aft from the bulkhead to form both sides of the rear passenger entrance. These are joined at the rear of the fuselage by a big circular firewall, which locates and surrounds the front end of the centre engine. The structure is finally stiffened by four quadrant-shaped, longitudinal torsion boxes; these are tapered fore-and-aft, and fit along the top and bottom edges of both main beams to complete the rounded cross-section of the fuselage. The space between the cantilevered beams is occupied by the box structure of the fin, the centre inlet duct and the hydraulically operated ventral stairway.

The tail

The vertical tail is more or less a conventional two-spar torsion box, but the forward spar is divided into two separate loadpaths at its lower end in order to pass each side of the central intake trunking. This big, inverted-Y assembly, is swept back at the extraordinary angle of 55° (far more sweep than the majority of jet fighters), and the whole thing is anchored to the rear pressure bulkhead, with attachment points at shoulder height on either side of the passenger door. The orthodox rear spar is some distance aft of the curved inlet duct, anchored to the two main box-beams and supported by the circular firewall. The torsion

box is completed by multiple plate ribs and a stiffened sheet skin.

The hinge-pin for the tailplane (stabiliser) operates in a transverse saddle-bearing at the top of the fin. The movable surface itself is a single-piece, two-spar carry-through structure, pivoted on its aerodynamic centre to provide trim limits of plus 4° to minus 12.5°. The rear spar carries all the brackets, hinges and control jacks for the elevator system, while the much lighter forward spar passes through a curved slot in the upper fin, to link-up with an electrically-driven, irreversible screwjack; the control mechanisms are covered by a two-piece fibreglass 'bullet' fairing, which extends aft to house the rear navigation lights and an optional HF antenna. Trimming movement is normally signalled by up/down 'pickle-switches' on each control yoke, but a back-up system of cables and conventional trim wheels is available in the event of an electrical failure. The balanced

elevators are actuated by duplicated hydraulic systems, and each surface incorporates a small control tab to provide automatic manual reversion.

The split rudder is mounted directly on the rear spar of the tail-fin. The two sections normally operate in tandem, but for maximum safety they use separate hydraulic systems, and each has its own yaw-damper channel (which is limited to only 4° of deflection). Both sections have enough individual power to counteract the yaw

of each yoke are then cone-bolted to a pair of mounting lugs on the engine-casing, with the primary load delivered just forward of the engine's centre-of-gravity. The single-point rear mounts (which take a lot less of the overall load) are incorporated into the box-beams on either side of the fuselage, and attached to the engine immediately in front of the reverser mechanism. The stub 'pylons' cover the actual mounting brackets, and carry all the engine-related services (fuel, electrics, instrumentation, fire detection/suppression, compressor bleed air) across the gap between the fuselage and the installed power unit. The cowlings are separate sub-assemblies, which can be hinged open or fully detached to allow maintenance access.

The centre engine is isolated from the main aircraft structure by vertical and horizontal firewalls, and the surrounding body panels are hinged upwards to provide access. The three-point mountings are virtually identical to those on the side engines, but the steel yokes are supported by a triangular sub-frame (almost a

generated by a side-engine failure. Anti-balance tabs were included in the design to reduce the overall size of the rudders, but there are no control tabs, and manual reversion is not available; instead, the system relies on the third (stand-by) hydraulic circuit which drives the lower section only. Artificial feel units are incorporated in both the rudder and elevator systems.

Engine Installation

All three Pratt & Whitney JT8D power units are mounted on the airframe in a similar fashion, but the forged-steel yokes for the side engines are attached horizontally, while the centre engine hangs from vertical yokes in the tail. Vibration-proof fixings are standard, with structural fuses built-in to ensure a clean breakaway in the event of catastrophic engine failure. The forward yokes for the side engines are diffused into the Section-46 pressure bulkhead; the upper and lower arms

Left:
TS-JHT was delivered to Tunis Air in June 1976, but it was leased to Sudan Airways in January 1983 and operated in this hybrid paint scheme for just over a year.
Hugh Newell

Right:
Before its involvement with international terrorism, Libya used to have a flourishing airline business. A UN embargo now prevents external flights, and Libyan Arab Airlines appears to be in a state of suspended animation. 5A-DIC was one of about a dozen 727-200s delivered during the 1970s, but without spares its condition must now be considered doubtful.
Hugh Newell

pylon) attached to the base of the rear fin. Air is drawn down to the engine through the curved S-duct, before passing through the vertical firewall and into the fan section of the engine itself. The shape of the upper intake scoop is built-up from a series of 'horseshoe' frames, which are joined to the forward fin spar as part of Section-48, and then covered with a light-alloy skin. The oval inlet cowl (circular on the more-powerful 727-200) is manufactured as a separate unit, and butt-jointed into its position above the rear of Section-46 during final-assembly of the four main body components. All three inlets are lined with acoustic panelling which is specially tuned to absorb most of the frequencies associated with the JT8D's 'fan-whine'.

Hydraulics

When it was first revealed in the early 1960s, the brilliant hydraulics system on the 727 was widely acknowledged to be among the best in the world — a reputation that seems to have lasted almost as long as the aircraft itself. It was loosely based on the much simpler 707 system, but several basic engineering changes were made as a result of earlier service experience. Troublesome banjo connectors, for instance, were completely eliminated from the 727, and the seamless steel pipes were made up into longer, pre-formed units, to minimise the number of potentially leaky couplings; the system filters were also moved to a position much closer to the primary pumps — a simple alteration, but one which later saved many hours of unnecessary circuit flushing whenever a pump failure occurred. The new features combined to create a commendably leak-free and maintenance-friendly system. Most of the beneficial design changes eventually found their way back into the four-jet programmes, and the basic architecture of the 727 became standard practice on all Boeing aircraft.

The tri-jet layout is a great deal more complicated than that of the 707. Systems 'A' and 'B' generally operate in tandem, but each is completely independent of the other, and both systems are energised by two entirely separate power sources. In addition to the two primaries, a third (stand-by) circuit — system 'C' — uses the B-system fluid reservoir and its own dedicated power-pack to drive a limited range of back-up services. The entire system uses fire-resistant Skydrol at a nominal pressure of 3,000lb sq/in. As far as possible, every major component was made line-replaceable, and primary hydraulic circuits; the elevators, inboard ailerons and outer ailerons all have twin-chamber (A plus B) jacks, but the rudder uses single-source jacks in separate circuits to power its upper and lower halves. The loss of a single pump in either primary system would therefore have virtually no effect; the loss of one complete system (a double pump failure) would simply

Left:
N4732 was an ex-National Airlines machine, acquired by Pan Am when the two airlines merged in January 1980. Most of these aircraft — all 200-series — were flown to Europe to replace the 727-100s on the German internal services. *Hugh Newell*

Below left:
CS-TBS shows the mid-1970s colour scheme of Transportes Aereos Portugueses — now known more simply as TAP-Air Portugal. *Hugh Newell*

cause a slight drop in available power, without reducing the effectiveness of the controls themselves. To lose both main systems at once, all four primary pumps would have to fail during a single flight. In this highly unlikely event, the pitch and roll axes would automatically revert to manual (tab) control, and the emergencies-only system-C would activate to power the leading-edge devices and lower rudder — although the rudder would lose its yaw-damper.

several are completely interchangeable — both within the aircraft itself, and in some cases between other airliners in the Boeing group. Reservoirs and pumps are mainly accessible through hatchways in the sides of the ventral stairway, and replenishment is pressure-fed from beneath the aircraft.

System-A is powered by two direct-drive mechanical pumps (on the port and centre engines), while system-B uses a pair of ac electrical pumps; the stand-by system is energised by a third (entirely separate) electric pump. Each movable surface in the main flight-control system is operated by actuators in both

The spoilers are split symmetrically between systems A and B, but no back-up is provided because operation of the panels is not critical to flight safety. All six Kruegers are powered by system-A, but the leading-edge slats are divided operationally into matched inner and outer pairs on each wing, and the system authority is split accordingly. None of the leading-edge devices is powered by both primary systems, but in each case the individual panels are included on the stand-by circuit. The trailing-edge flap groups are all driven by system-A, with back-up power provided by the co-located electric motors. The ventral air-stairs are raised and lowered as part of system-B, but any failure on such a non-critical facility has to be overcome by hard work and a secondary hand pump!

Undercarriage

The undercarriage is a major user of hydraulic power. Most of the actuators (including doors, extension/retraction of all three units, nose wheel steering and nosewheel braking) are part of system-A, but the mainwheel brakes are operated by system B. No back-up power is provided for door and leg operation, but each leg can be lowered by gravity if necessary, and then locked into the 'three greens' position by an on-board hand-crank. The only difference between this and the powered system is that the mainwheel doors do not re-close around the extended leg. Emergency braking is available as part of system-C, but the aircraft is more than capable of stopping under the influence of reverse-thrust alone. Nosewheel steering to and from the runway is controlled by a tiller system mounted on each cockpit sidewall, but 6° of movement either side of the centreline is available through the rudder pedals, and this gives a much more natural sense of directional control during take-off and landing.

The main components of the undercarriage were designed for a working life of 60,000 landings, with an initial 8,000 between the planned replacement of minor parts such as bearings, pins and bushes. All three pairs of wheels are fitted with Goodrich multi-disc brakes (and Hydro-Aire anti-skid systems), and these were cleared for 600 stops before pad replacement or disc inspections. Rolling wheel life (an important element of short-range operations) was set at the unusually high figure of 10,000 miles — representing perhaps 1,000 flights.

Electrics

The overall electrical configuration was also based on that of the 707, but a centralised check-out panel was added, and cooling of the 727 generators was much improved as a direct result of 707 service experience. All three 727 engines carry a Sundstrand constant-speed unit coupled to a 40kVA brushless generator, which provides 115/200V three-phase at 400cps: dc power is derived from three 50A

transformer/rectifiers. Stand-by power is available in dc from a 22A-hr Ni-Cd battery, which is also coupled to a 250VA inverter to provide an ac output for vital flight instruments. Full circuit-breaker protection is available via the engineer's panel, and an essential ac bus can distribute power for safe flight even when the rest of the system is shut down.

Standard ARINC packaging for electrical control units has been used wherever possible, and all wiring is routed through 'raceway' ducts or protective conduits; approximately 10% of the wires in each bundle are spare. Identical crimped-contact connectors were used throughout the aircraft to eliminate the need for special assembly and repair tools. Plugs and sockets were also standardised, and multi-pin disconnects allow all major panels to be removed for bench maintenance. The primary electrical 'consumers' on board include the forward air-stairs (optional), galley unit (16kVA as standard, but a 24kVA unit is available as an option), tailplane trim, cockpit de-ice/de-mist, air-conditioning fans, fuel and hydraulic pumps, internal and external lighting, avionics and radar, flight instrumentation, and stand-by power for the trailing-edge flap actuators. The optional auxiliary power unit (APU) is linked to a fourth 40kVA generator but this cannot be operated in flight, and is generally restricted to the supply of lighting and air-conditioning power during turnaround.

Fuel

Most of the fuel on the 727 is carried inside the visible part of the wing, but about 15% of the total is stored in the central carry-through structure — hidden beneath the reinforced section of the cabin floor. The port and starboard outer-wing tanks (Nos 1 and 3) are virtually identical, self-contained units, each side holding 1,700 US gal (1,416 Imp) in a single compartment occupying about 75% of the semi-span; the structural ribs inside the tanks are fully perforated to ensure adequate flow between individual bays, but they also act as effective baffles against the 'sloshing' of fuel during aircraft manoeuvres. The wing tips — which are well aft of the engine inlets — each incorporate a small surge tank, together with the outlet valves for the fuel dumping system. The central No 2 tank runs right through the fuselage from one inner-wing space to the other, and consists of either four or five interlinked chambers, depending on customer options. The main body of fuel is stored in the wing-roots —

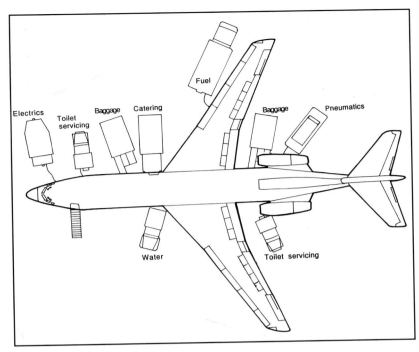

Electrics
Toilet servicing
Baggage
Catering
Fuel
Baggage
Pneumatics
Water
Toilet servicing

suffers an in-flight failure, the other can take over and supply fully conditioned air for the whole aircraft. The right-hand (starboard) system is controlled from the passenger cabin, but the left provides a proportion of its output to the flightdeck, so the mixing valve is operated solely by the flight engineer. The limiting pressure differential is 8.6lb/sq in — which normally provides a cabin altitude of just over 5,000ft during a long-range cruise at maximum altitude.

where the sealed torsion-box is at its widest and deepest. These two bays are separated from the outer wing by solid (unperforated) ribs, but they are permanently connected to each other, and to a pair of rubberised, flexible cells in the centre-section; this basic, four-bay arrangement, forms a single big tank with a total capacity of 3,600 US gal (2,997 Imp). To meet the longer range requirements of some customers, a third flexible cell was added to the centre-section of some aircraft, raising the total capacity by another 500 US gal (416 Imp). The entire system of up to 7,500 US gal (6,245 Imp) can be replenished in about 12min, using pressure-refuelling sockets under the leading-edge of the starboard wing.

Air-conditioning

The Pratt & Whitney JT8D was the first American engine designed from the outset for direct compressor-bleed into an aircraft pressurisation system. On the 727 the basic flow is drawn from the 8th stages of both outer engines (Nos 1 and 3), but an automated boost system can provide additional air from the two 13th stages when demand exceeds supply. The centre (No 2) engine provides a back-up source of 8th-stage air only. The raw supply is pre-cooled by heat-exchangers in the side-engine struts, before being ducted into identical port or starboard conditioning units; if either of these plants

Distribution within the cabin is similar to the 707's 'hot-wall' system, which ducts conditioned air up between the window units to discharge immediately beneath the hat rack. An additional overhead duct on the 727 runs the whole length of the cabin ceiling; this is capable of delivering large quantities of hot or cold air on demand, and is hugely welcomed by passengers and crew alike — especially during turnarounds in extreme climatic conditions. Both cargo compartments are heated and pressurised by 'used' cabin air, which is continually drawn through slots in the floor/wall intersection as it makes its way down to the twin outflow valves in the rear hold. Controllable cold-air nozzles are provided in every passenger-service module and at all crew stations, including the galley. During turnround operations the entire system can be run from an external ground cart if necessary, or from on-board electrical fans powered by the APU.

Water and Oxygen

The passengers and crew are provided with separate emergency oxygen supplies, which become available at a cabin altitude of 14,000ft — or on crew command, whichever occurs first. The passenger arrangement includes two 114cu/ft high pressure gaseous cylinders, which

typically feed four drop-down face masks for every overhead service unit; the deployment, pressure-reduction and flow-regulation functions are normally fully automatic, but the whole system (or even single masks in the case of illness) can be triggered by the crew whenever necessary. The system for the crew is essentially the same as that for the passengers, but the container capacity is generally limited to 76cu/ft (a 114cu/ft system is available, but only as a customer option). All three storage cylinders are housed in the air-conditioning 'snake-pit', in the pressurised underfloor area of Section-43.

Potable water for drinking fountains, wash basins, toilet units and the galley is stored in a single 40 US gals (33 Imp) titanium tank, which is internally pressurised by engine bleed air up to a maximum of 25lb sq/in. This continuous 'top-pressure' method of distribution avoids the complication of a separate pump at each outlet, but the pipework, connections and seals all needed careful attention during the design phase to ensure that the system remained leakproof. The main tank is replenished through an airtight valve in the side of the fuselage, and the whole system eventually drains into separate collector-tanks at the front and rear of the aircraft. A small electrical pump provides compressed air while the main engines are shut down.

Cockpit

The cockpit equipment on the 727 has undergone many changes over the years, but most of the original aircraft were fitted with a near-copy of the highly successful 707 layout. Apart from the usual flight instruments, standard ARINC 'boxes' included a 542 flight recorder; twin VHF communication radios; twin VHF navigation systems (both with glideslope); two ADFs; two DMEs and two ATC transponders. Sperry supplied both yaw-damper systems, twin vertical (attitude) gyros and twin C-10 compasses; and Collins provided the flight directors and a marker-beacon receiver. Optional equipment included LORAN; dual HF (with its characteristic 'stinger' aerial in the tail fairing); dual Doppler and dual radio altimeters. Further options — such as a glideslope facility on the flight directors; a third attitude gyro; and a third VHF nav or VHF comms — improved the existing fit, while others added new (and sometimes expensive) facilities to an already

well-equipped aircraft. This latter group included an instrument comparison and warning system; and an early example of the now-familiar cockpit voice recorder; variable instrument switching; an autothrottle and a speed-command system.

The Sperry SP-50 analogue autopilot was a big departure from the 707's Bendix unit. Specially designed for the 727, the SP-50 operates in pitch and roll to hold selected altitudes, headings and/or pitch attitudes: it also provides Doppler heading control, together with the normal VOR/Tacan and ILS functions. Both channels (aileron and elevator) can be engaged independently, and the tailplane motor can be coupled to the system to provide a degree of auto-trim. The yaw-dampers are separate sub-systems; these operate rapidly and completely autonomously within their given range, and none of the 'twitchy' feedback reaches the rudder pedals.

Vital statistics

The basic weights, dimensions and performance indicators of the 727 have been quoted in many forms during the life of the aircraft, and most of the published tables seem to disagree in one way or another – particularly in the field of operational performance. The following figures are therefore a digest of previously circulated information, designed and laid-out to provide a reasonable guide only to the original, short-bodied aircraft (later known as the 727-100).

Wing span: 108ft 0in
Chord (at the root): 25ft 3in, (at the tip) 7ft 8in
Wing Area: 1,650 sq/ft
Thickness/chord ratio: from 13% at the root
   to 9% at the tip
Aspect ratio: 7.5
Sweepback at quarter-chord: 32°
Angle of incidence: 2°
Dihedral: 3°
Overall length (including tail): 134ft 4in

Fuselage length: 116ft 2in
Overall height: 34ft 0in
Tailplane span: 35ft 9in
Wheel track: 18ft 9in
Wheelbase: 53ft 3in
Minimum turn radius (main gear to opposite elevator tip): 70ft 4in

Internal cabin: length 71ft 8in
Usable height: 7ft 2in
Maximum width: 11ft 7in
Volume (excluding flightdeck): 5,000 cu/ft
Floor area: 766 sq/ft
Typical passenger loads: 70 1st class, 114 tourist, 94 mixed
Usable baggage volume: 855 cu/ft

Initial max take-off weight: 142,000lb
  (standard aircraft): wing loading 86lb sq/ft
Optional max take-off weight: 152,000lb
  (with long-range tank):
  wing loading 92lb sq/ft
100-series later cleared to: 160,000lb
  (with structural improvements)

Take-off distance at 142,000lb:
  5,5000ft (standard atmosphere/20° flap)
  6,600ft (ICAN+41°F/20° flap)
Take-off distance at 152,000lb:
  6,300ft (standard atmosphere/20° flap)
  8,200ft (ICAN+41°F/10° flap)
Take-off distance at 160,000lb:
  8,100ft (standard atmosphere/10°flap)

9,500ft (ICAN+41°F/10° flap)
Economical cruising speeds:
  390kt e.a.s. below 21,000ft;
  Mach 0.88 above 21,000ft
Maximum high-speed cruise:
  511kt (589mph)at 130,000lb and 21,000ft;
  519kt (59mph) at 110,000lb and 23,000ft
Maximum permitted speeds:
  Mach 0.95/567kt (653mph)
Normal service ceiling: 36,000ft

*Approximate full-reserves range
  with 25,000lb payload:* 2,000 miles
*Approximate full-reserves range with full fuel/
  14,500lb payload:* 2,400 miles

Initial maximum landing weight: 131,000lb
  Later cleared to 135,000lb after structural
  improvements
Approach speeds (sea-level/full flap):
  120kt (138mph) at 130,000lb;
  100kt (115mph) at 90,000lb
CAR landing-field length (sea level):
  4,950ft at 130,000lb 3,950ft at 90,000lb
Stalling speeds:
  94kt (108mph) at 131,000lb
  89kt (102mph) at 125,000lb

Below:
G-BCDA was one of several ex-Japan Airlines 727-100s operated by Dan-Air. These aircraft had additional emergency exits aft of the wing (unusual in the shorter fuselage), and the UK authorities insisted that a stick-pusher was added to the stall protection system.
Hugh Newell

Above:
The 727 cargo door is virtually identical to that used on the four-engined Boeing 707. Before joining the Royal New Zealand AF in July 1981, this 100-series Convertible was N7435U of United Airlines. *Hugh Newell*

727C (Convertible)

Announced at the beginning of August 1964, the 727C represented the first significant change to the basic 727 airframe. The new model was fitted with an 86in high by 134in wide cargo door in the left-hand side of the forward fuselage; a full-length cargo-conveyor system capable of handling up to eight pre-loaded pallets; and a strengthened cabin floor to absorb the higher load-concentrations of a cargo-type operation. All the doors and emergency exits of the passenger model were retained untouched. The cargo door, together with its machined-alloy frame and all the complex operating and locking mechanisms, were identical in virtually every respect to the upwards-opening door developed for the 707.

The revised aircraft was designed to offer adaptable cabin arrangements for all-passenger, all-cargo or mixed passenger/cargo operations — depending in the main on seasonal changes of demand on an existing route network. Reconfiguration from one layout to another was usually possible in about two hours, and typical payload variations included 94 mixed-class (first/tourist) passengers; eight pallets with a maximum combined weight of 36,750lb; or a compound load consisting of 52 tourist-class seats in the rear compartment and four pallets (24,000lb) in the front. The 727C was initially certified for take-off at 160,000lb — which at that time was the upper limit for any 727 — but further strengthening of the centre-section and undercarriage allowed some of the later examples to operated at up to 169,000lb.

The first order for Convertibles was placed by Northwest Orient Airlines, followed by Lufthansa, United, Braniff, Pan American, Eastern and TWA. Between them, these seven carriers eventually accounted for more than 65% of all cargo-door production — with United and Eastern leading the pack on final totals of 41 and 25 aircraft respectively. The first to be manufactured was slot No 211 on the 727 line, which was originally earmarked for N490US, a standard passenger-jet option reserved by Northwest Orient. The specification was changed by the firm order, and the slot was transferred over to Boeing 'ownership' before completion. A cargo door was fitted, and the airframe finally emerged as the company development machine, N7270C. This aircraft flew for the first time on 30 December 1965, and the certification trials were essentially complete by the beginning of April the following year. In the meantime several other Convertibles had flown, and deliveries to Northwest began on 13 April — with airframe No 244 carrying the reallocated registration N490US. The company 'prototype' went on to conduct a further series of development trials (mainly on the later 727QC and 727M specifications), before being refurbished to full airline standard and offered on the open leasing market.

727QC (Quick Change)

The 727QC was built to virtually the same fuselage specification as the 727C, but the interior fittings were specially engineered to take advantage of short-term (as opposed to seasonal) variations in traffic demand. This generally allowed passengers to be carried during the popular daylight hours, and cargo operations to be flown at night — something that could not be done profitably with the 727C, because of its relatively long conversion time. Instead of the piecemeal removal of individual seat-rows, galley units, carpets and floor panels, all the floor-level cabin furnishings of the 727QC were mounted directly on to 11 pallet-style bases. These were unlocked as complete units, trundled through the fuselage on the cargo-conveyor system, and then withdrawn from the aircraft sideways through the big cargo door; some airlines even went so far as to unload the 'furniture' directly into a specially-built truck, which housed the entire contents of a single aircraft in the correct order, allowing rapid reconfiguration to whatever standard was required. A well-drilled crew could strip-out and prepare a QC to receive its first pallets in less than 30min, leaving all the interior units to be cleaned and replenished by staff on the

ground, while the aircraft itself was away on an out-and-return cargo run

Although the Convertible and Quick Change models were designed for very similar operations, there was less headroom in the QC and the aircraft could not be used for unrestricted interline flights (where pre-loaded pallets were transferred from one aircraft to another, or even from one airline to another, for onward shipment to a final destination). The overhead hat racks were completely removed from the cabin of the 727C as part of the role-conversion process; this was a time-consuming business, involving the disconnection of all emergency-oxygen, fresh-air and electrical feeds to the individual passenger-service units (PSUs). The resulting total strip-down created a cabin cross-section identical to that of a cargo 707, and marginally bigger than that of a DC-8, which allowed the Convertible to be used as a feeder aircraft for most long-haul routes. The disconnection of PSUs was impossible in the limited time available for QC conversion, so the overhead racks were retained on the aircraft, but modified to unclip from their normal position and fold upwards into the ceiling. This system restricted the loading height along both sides of

Below:
This Tunis Air 200-series aircraft shows the outwards-opening doors to both underfloor baggage holds (the equivalent doors on the smaller 100-series open inwards). *Hugh Newell*

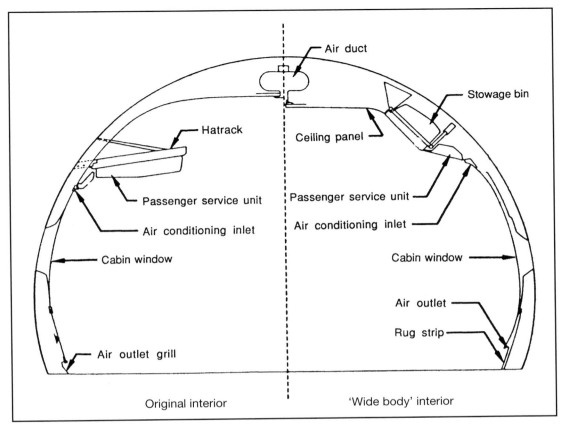

Air duct

Stowage bin

Hatrack

Ceiling panel

Passenger service unit

Passenger service unit

Air conditioning inlet

Air conditioning inlet

Cabin window

Cabin window

Air outlet

Rug strip

Air outlet grill

Original interior

'Wide body' interior

Above:
The 'wide-body' style interior was originally offered as an option, but it later became standard fit.

the cabin, and reduced the usable cargo volume by about 15%. Some airlines refused to buy the QC for this reason, but most accepted the loss of headroom as a trade-off against ease of conversion, and simply changed the rules for loading each pallet.

As a measure of their confidence in the aircraft, several carriers switched existing orders and options for the 727C, over to the slightly more-expensive QC (in some cases, part-way through a production run). Such changes were not always reported by Boeing, which makes confirmation of the exact production-split between the two models almost impossible. The company still confirms that 164 short-bodied 727s were actually built with a cargo-door installed, and it now seems certain that about two-thirds of these emerged as factory-fitted QCs. Several in-service Convertibles were also upgraded later to full-QC standard. In addition to all the new-build aircraft, a large number of

original passenger models have been converted over the years to some kind of cargo configuration — not necessarily by Boeing, or to an exact Boeing specification. These aircraft generally retain a residual passenger-carrying capability, and are often referred to (now) as 727-100Cs or 727-100QCs. The final stage of conversion — which was never a new-build programme — involves the complete removal of all passenger facilities, including windows and most emergency exits; these 'full-time' freighters are generally (although unofficially) designated 727-100Fs.

The first Boeing-manufactured QC was N7401U (line No 250) for United Airlines. It flew for the first time on 7 April 1966, and after a brief period of certification trials it was delivered on 15 May to begin several weeks of ad-hoc crew-training and route-proving flights — mainly to familiarise out-station ground crews with the conversion technique and cargo-handling system. Two more aircraft were delivered during the training period, and the type finally went into service on 8 August, initially on the busy route between Chicago and New York.

Low level production of the short-bodied cargo aircraft continued at Seattle until early 1971. The final pair were QCs destined for South African Airlines (ZS-SBH and ZS-SBI); these were delivered in February and March of that year and were among the very last batch of 727-100s to be manufactured before the stretched 200-series monopolised the line.

727M (Military)

The projected military version of the 727C was much in evidence during the mid-1960s, but is almost forgotten today. The full military specification was never flown, but the aircraft was offered to several friendly governments for roles such as assault, staff and command transport; flight refuelling tanker; medevac missions and carrier on-board delivery! Extensive trials were completed with the 'prototype' cargo-door aircraft (N7270C), including military parachuting through the ventral passenger door, and simulated carrier landings which brought the 100,00lb machine to a full stop in less than 700ft. Plans for the production aircraft included a military-standard load-deck; a much stronger undercarriage to allow landings at up to 165,00lb; a modified ventral door and (possibly) a nose-leg catapult bar and arrester hook for the COD version. In the event, little interest was shown by US forces, and the project was dropped before any serious engineering work was done.

727-200

When it came to developing the passenger-carrying potential of the 727, Boeing began by adopting the simplest possible formula to arrive at a high-capacity, short-range 'airbus' version. All the basic systems and aerodynamics of the original were retained virtually untouched, but the fuselage was stretched by 20ft to provide space for about eight additional seat rows. The new aircraft was designated 727-200, and its introduction led to the shorter-fuselage models being renumbered (sometimes retrospectively) as the 100-series.

The extra fuselage frames were applied equally fore and aft of the wing, and each 10ft 'plug' consisted of passenger accommodation above the floor and uncluttered luggage space below. Other changes in the airframe included two additional emergency-exit/service-doors in the rear of the cabin, close to the side engine inlets; an extra (outwards opening) door into the expanded rear luggage hold; modified trailing-edge flap supports; and a revised profile to the wing/fuselage fairing. The galley unit and its dedicated service door (still an approved emergency exit) were moved forward to a new position just behind the cockpit, and the oval centre-engine inlet was replaced by a larger, circular version, in anticipation of Pratt & Whitney upgrading the power of the JT8D engine.

Typical passenger accommodation at 34in pitch (all tourist-class) went up from about 120 in the original aircraft, to nearly 170 in the extended cabin; the maximum permitted seating (dictated by the relevant safety certificates) increased from 131 to 189. These higher figures improved basic seat-mile costs by anything up to 20%, but the lack of a fully-developed engine limited the take-off performance of the new aircraft and imposed a maximum weight of 169,000lb — the same as a high-gross-weight version of the 727-100. The increased structural weight of the longer fuselage represented a much higher proportion of available take-off weight, and this formula inevitably restricted either the payload or the amount of fuel that could be carried for each departure. The tankage arrangements (including the optional centre tank) were virtually the same for both aircraft, but the stretched version could only carry fuel for 1,600 miles when it was operating at its maximum payload of 39,340lb. If range was essential for particular routes, full tanks could provide up to 2,550 miles — but under these circumstances the weight of fuel on board for take-off limited the payload to just over 25,000lb.

The availability of the 727-200 was announced by Seattle during the first week of August 1965. At that time more than 160 standard aircraft had already been delivered; a further 100 were either being constructed or awaiting their turn on the assembly line, and new orders were still arriving in the Sales Office at the same rate as completed aircraft were leaving the factory. Detail design and tooling for the stretched version took just over a year, and construction of the Boeing-owned 'prototype' began in September 1966. The completed aircraft (N7270L) was formally rolled-out on 29 June 1967, and the 475hr test programme began with a two-hour maiden flight on 27 July. The FAA passenger-carrying certificate was finally issued on 30 November 1967.

Initial sales of the 200-series were all to US domestic carriers, with Northeast Airlines (now part of Delta) launching the programme with an order for six; these were followed by orders from

Left:
The 200-series 727 is 20ft longer than the baseline aircraft (10ft fore and aft of the wing), and the rear fuselage has an extra Type1 emergency exit on each side. The starboard galley-service door is also moved forward, and the centre-engine inlet has a revised, circular shape. *Hugh Newell*

Below:
Take-off rotation brings the tail engine of the longer-fuselage 727-200 perilously close to the runway, but damage is prevented by a hydraulically-activated bumper.

Bottom:
With nine emergency exists (including the rear entrance door) the 727-200 is licensed to carry up to 189 passengers. This particular arrangement shows 180 seats, but most of the original carriers contented themselves with about 170 at 34in pitch.

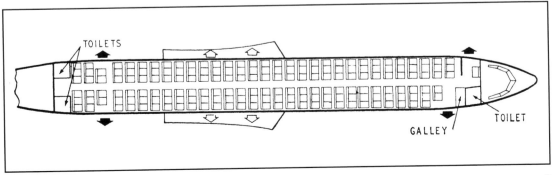

TOILETS

TOILET

GALLEY

Top:
Originally operated by Lufthansa/Condor as D-ABIP, this 100-series aircraft was acquired by the Brithin company in 1982. After conversion to VIP standard, it was allocated the registration VR-BHN. *Hugh Newell*

Above:
This unusual 727-100VIP is one of the few 727s that were purchased direct from the Renton assembly line as a private jet. Most similar aircraft (there are now more than 50 in regular use) have been converted from redundant airline stock. This particular example was first delivered to the ITT Corporation as N320HG in November 1971. *Hugh Newell*

Below:
After three years carrying passengers for Singapore Airlines, 727-200 9V-SGF was converted to VIP standard and re-registered HZ-DA5 in April 1985. The unusual window configuration seen here suggests that the cabin has been divided into several discreet compartments. The lack of colour-highlighting around the emergency exits is permissible (though still inadvisable) if the aircraft is not licensed to carry fare-paying passengers. *Hugh Newell*

Above:
When Wistair International ordered this executive version of the Advanced 727-200 on 24 September 1980, it became the 100th individual customer for the 727. Seen here in the livery of Wedge Aviation Inc of Houston, Texas, the aircraft was specially configured for transatlantic operation, and incorporated an extra 3,300 US gal tank in the rear underfloor cargo compartment.

Below:
The first of the real heavyweight 727s was this Advanced 200series aircraft for Sterling Airways (OY-SAU). These machines were fitted with 16,000lb-thrust JT8D-17s, heavier undercarriage support beams, and were initially cleared to take-off at 208,000lb (later increased to 210,000lb). With weights such as these, Sterling was able to uplift sufficient fuel to carry 189 passengers direct from Scandinavia to the Canary Islands – a sector length of some 2,500nm.

National (25), American (22), Continental (five) and United (six) — and then by Air France, which became the first overseas buyer when it ordered four in July 1966. Deliveries began immediately after certification, and by the end of 1967 Northeast and National had both received their first three aircraft.

The 200-series dominated the Seattle factory throughout 1968 and 1969, but new orders became increasingly hard to find in a recession-hit industry, and by the beginning of 1970 combined production of all four 727 models (100, 100C, 100QC and 200) had fallen to just six aircraft per month. A new widebody-style interior and noise-abating 'hush-kits' were offered on the -200 from mid-1969, but these

failed to inject new life into the programme, and deliveries continued to outstrip new sales. The 100-series was dropped altogether in late 1970, and at last the 200-series was redesigned to give it the range and airfield performance it so obviously needed.

727BJ (Business Jet)

Although it was never accepted as an official designation, the BJ suffix was frequently used in books and magazines to describe a corporate version of the 727 — initially referring to the short-body 100-series, but later to the stretched-fuselage 200-series. Unencumbered by airliner-type furnishings, the business-jet was much lighter in its basic ready-for-service form (even with a luxury interior fitted), and both versions had a huge amount of disposable underfloor space to accommodate extra fuel and avionics. Flexible bag-tanks in each luggage compartment increased the standard fuel capacity to nearly 11,000 US gal, which guaranteed an all-weather transatlantic range while carrying a 4,000lb payload. Long-range, over-water navigation was improved by the

installation of dual INS, an upgraded autopilot and a military-style 'long-reach' weather radar.

The first (and only) new-build 100-series business-jet was ordered by the ITT Corporation on 13 November 1970. The aircraft was delivered as N320HG during November 1971, and has the distinction of being the very last of 571 short-bodied 727s produced by Boeing. A total of eight 200-series BJs were ordered direct from the factory between 1973 and 1982 — most of them going into long-term service as government or presidential transports. In addition to the nine brand-new aircraft, about 50 ex-airline 727s have been converted to VIP standard over the years, and the list is still growing. These have comprised all the basic models (including those with a cargo door), but not all of them were converted to exactly the same engineering specification.

Advanced 727-200

During 1969 and early 1970 Boeing began to scrap some of the tooling needed for high-volume 727 production. The aircraft itself had acquired an excellent reputation for reliability and performance, but the design was 10 years old and it was facing stiff competition from improved models of the DC-9 and BAC-111; it was also about to meet the first generation of medium-range wide-bodied jets (DC-10-10, TriStar and A300B) in a head-to-head contest that could decide fleet acquisition policies for many years ahead.

The stretched 727 fuselage was always thought by Seattle to be about the right size for most city-pair applications, but the aircraft itself lacked the power to compete on realistic terms with most of its newer rivals. If the downward sales trend was to be reversed in any significant way, more thrust would have to be found from somewhere. More-powerful engines would increase the usable take-off weight, improve time-to-height climbing performance, and sustain the cruise at higher, more-economical altitudes. The programme to achieve these goals was provisionally described under the in-house title 'Advanced 727' — a name that somehow remained with the aircraft throughout it later production life.

The standard powerplant at the beginning of 1969 was the 14,000lb thrust JT8D-9. The

Above:
Seen here without engines during a major overhaul, this 'white-tail' Advanced 727-200 is (or rather was) a real hot-ship among 727s. It was originally one of 12 aircraft supplied to Mexicana with a solid-fuel rocket motor installed under the fuselage. The rocket was available as a contingency power-pack for departures from airfields in the high Andes; it was only ever used in situations of dire emergency, but its installation required the re-location of several radio and electronic systems — most of which were transferred to a new equipment bay in the top of the fuselage. This unique sub-type was sometimes referred to unofficially as the 727-200/JATO, but the name was never formally adopted by Boeing. A few have now moved on to other carriers, but they can still be recognised by slight discontinuities in the normally-straight roof line. *Hugh Newell*

Above:
Photographed at Renton during the first week of August 1973, three Braniff 727-200s (N419BN, N420BN and N421BN) share the ramp with an unidentified 'green' aircraft, which is clearly awaiting its first visit to the paint shop. The unfinished aircraft is not built to the Braniff specification, because it has an extra passenger window close to the forward door.

Right:
The 1,000th 727 was N474DA, an Advanced 200-series aircraft destined for service with Delta Airlines. It was completed in early December 1973, and is seen here in a deliberately anonymous-looking version of its future owner's livery (the airline title and the dark blue section of the Delta logo are all missing from the fin and forward fuselage). Instead of the single airline name, the sides of the forward passenger cabin are decorated with the insignia of more than 50 separate customers. The 727 was the first commercial jet in the world to reach such a significant production milestone.

Above:
During 1981 no fewer than 257 airliners of all the major types were cleared through the Boeing Test Center, including at least 94 727-200s. A close examination of this picture (probably taken in May 1981) reveals examples from WesternAirlines, Mexicana, Avianca, Continental, American Airlines, and two unidentified aircraft which were too far away to read the company titles.

15,000lb JT8D-11 was also available as a customer-option, but the take-off benefits derived from its extra power were generally dissipated by increased fuel consumption in the cruise. Alternative engines were not immediately available — although plans for a radically new version of the JT8D, with hollow air-cooled turbine blades and several other technical changes, were known to exist. This new specification (the proposed JT8D-15, initially rated at 15,500lb thrust) seemed to offer all the power and development potential needed for the Advanced aircraft, but Pratt & Whitney steadfastly refused to proceed with the project until a significant launch order was placed. Boeing had great faith in the future of a rejuvenated 727, and at the end of 1969 paid deposits on 30 engines straight from the drawing board.

The JT8D-15 became the centrepiece of an improvement programme that ultimately gave the 727 nearly 50% more range. The increased power allowed the aircraft's maximum take-off weight to go from 169,000lb to 191,000lb in virtually one step — clearing the way for a much heavier fuel load without sacrificing either airfield performance or payload capacity. The Advanced model was able to carry 8,090 US gal in its sealed wing and centre-section tanks (roughly the same as a then standard 727-200), but the new, more flexible weight limits, made it possible to include up to 2,480 US gal of additional fuel in a series of optional flexi-tanks. These were housed in the forward and/or aft luggage compartments, and owed much of their modular design to the earlier demand for long-range business jets.

Aircraft noise had become a global problem by the end of the 1960s, and it was clear to Boeing that a heavier and more-powerful 727 would not compare favourably with some of the newer airliners on offer — especially those equipped with early versions of the 'big fan' engines. More than $7 million was spent on a state-of-the art acoustics laboratory at Seattle, and the results of its work were fed straight back into all the active production programmes. On the Advanced 727, all three inlet cowls were modified to incorporate a new polymide sound-deadening material; this was specially developed in the company lab, and had a significant softening effect on the JT8D's irritating fan whine. Pratt & Whitney conducted a parallel research programme, and eventually developed a full acoustic treatment for the fan-case and by-pass duct of the engine itself. To complete the job, the harsh environment of the tail pipes were all surrounded by Boeing-designed 'hot end' sound absorbers, based on multiple layers of perforated steel. The end product of all this painstaking effort was one of the quietest aircraft of its era — particularly during the sensitive airfield-approach phase, which always seems to generate more community complaints than take-off.

In addition to new engines and the sound-attenuation measures, the Advanced package also included larger tyres and more-powerful brakes (to cope with the abandoned take-off case at higher gross weights); thicker machined wing planks and a beefed-up centre-section structure; better protection against corrosion; and the so-called 'Superjet' widebody interior (which was also available as a fleet-matching retrofit for all existing 727-200s). Some of the cockpit instrumentation was slightly upgraded, and a computerised flight-management system was offered for the first time as a customer option.

The new model was announced to the press during December 1970, together with news of the first few sales. The Japanese carrier All Nippon launched the programme with an order for three, and the Australian 'twins' (Ansett and ANA) followed with an order for four each; Tunis Air then upgraded an existing order (its first for any 727), asking for the new specification instead of the standard 200-series. The first Advanced aircraft was rolled-out in All Nippon colours as JA8342, but this registration was not used by the airline: instead, the 'prototype' was re-registered to Boeing (as N1790B) for its first flight on 29 February 1972, and was then allocated JA8343 immediately prior to delivery on 30 June.

The combination of good operating economics and a low first price made the Advanced aircraft an immediate success. After several exceptionally lean years (727 sales had slumped to just 26 in 1971), orders began to flood in: 119 were sold in 1972, and the period 1973-1978 averaged over 100 per year — with 1977 claiming the best results for a very long time, with 133 confirmed orders and almost as many options. Factory activity too, increased dramatically after the Advanced model was announced. From a base of three standard 727-200s per month during 1971, the line gradually accelerated to 9.5 by 1978, and eventually peaked at 11.5 to clear a growing backlog of orders during 1979/80. The new aircraft quickly became the only 727 available

active for an astonishing 14 more years, and the Advanced aircraft finally outsold all the other models put together. The specification was updated several times during its long production run, and a number of 'specials' were manufactured for individual airlines. In 1971, for example, Iberia ordered a lightweight (185,000lb) version, and when the 16,000lb thrust JT8D-17 was offered as an option in 1973, the Danish carrier Sterling AW used it as the basis of a heavyweight version, capable of carrying a full load of 189 passengers over the 2,500nm sector between Copenhagen and the Canary Islands. This aircraft had thicker wing planks and a stronger undercarriage, and its maximum take-off weight was increased to 208,000lb — a weight that was subsequently adopted as

Above:
The first long-body 727-200 (N290AS) for Alaska Airlines photographed on a Boeing production test flight.

Below:
The collapse of Braniff in 1982, and the subsequent sale of its fleet of low-time 727-200s, may well have precipitated the final end of 727 production. N467BN was delivered in February 1979, but is currently one of hundreds of airliners laid up in the southern deserts of the USA. *Peter Gilchrist*

direct from the factory; production of the original 200-series was discontinued in 1972 (after the completion of 306 airframes), and all orders and options existing at that time were automatically upgraded to the new standard.

After being almost written-off as a dying programme in 1970, the 727 line remained

standard for all Advanced 727s. The normal production aircraft were fitted with a new, more-efficient anti-skid system from 1973 onwards, and the thrust-reversers were improved in 1975, when the original external deflector doors were replaced by a much simpler cascade system. The cascade reverser offered greatly reduced

Above:
Ordered at the 1979 Paris Air Show, N715RC was the first of four 727-200s for the newly-formed US regional carrier, Republic Airlines. The new company was the result of a merger between Southern Airways and North Central Airlines – both of which were big operators of the DC9.

maintenance costs, and it was later widely adopted as a retrofit for all 727 models (including some of the original 100-series).

The new JT8D-17R received its FAA certificate in November 1976; this derivative engine was given 400lb more basic thrust than the earlier -17, but its real significance lay in the fact that it was fitted as standard with an automatic power reserve (APR) system, which increased the guaranteed airfield performance by a considerable margin. The system worked by sensing the early signs of failure in any one of the three engines during take-off; if a failure was confirmed, the APR reacted by automatically boosting the thrust-output of the two remaining engines. No pilot input was needed, and the contingency rating of 17,400lb thrust per engine remained available until the aircraft had reached a safe speed and altitude. The -17R was not adopted as standard equipment but several carriers — particularly those operating from hot-and-high or small airfields — chose it as an option.

It was inevitable that time would catch up with the 727 one day. Production was maintained at a reasonably high level until the end of 1980, but the order situation was already showing signs of a terminal decline. All major changes to the programme were dropped in 1978 because the twin-engined 757 (a new-technology replacement, based to a surprising degree on 727 components) was beginning to absorb more and more of the company's design and marketing capacity. Orders for the Advanced 727 continued to trickle in until 1981, but the financial collapse of Braniff AW in October that year left 19 existing production slots cancelled, and put about 60 used aircraft up for emergency disposal by the liquidators. The Braniff fleet included many well-maintained, low-time aircraft, and the sudden glut of good second-hand bargains put paid to the market for new aircraft almost overnight.

The last passenger model to be produced was number 1,817 on the assembly line. This aircraft was originally ordered by Iraqi AW (customer code 70), but political problems prevented its normal delivery and it was finally sold (along with several other 'problem' airframes) at a knock-down price to US Air. It first flew as N779AL, and was delivered to the airline of 6 April 1983.

727-200F

Much to everyone's surprise, Boeing introduced yet another model to the 727 range in October 1981 — just as the tri-jet line was drawing to a close. The 727-200F was designed from the outset as a pure freighter version of the

Above:
Air Charter International (ACI) was originally formed as a wholly-owned subsidiary of Air France, but in 1977 Air Inter was allowed to take a 20% share, and this is now reflected in the aircraft livery. ACI has its own Boeing customer code (X3), and in 1980 it independently ordered two Advanced 727-200s to operate alongside a small, existing fleet of ex-Air France 727-228s.

Below:
The 727 is now a popular aircraft for business or even personal use. This 200-series shows the registration N359PA (formerly used by a 100-series owned by Pan Am), but is otherwise anonymous. *Hugh Newell*

Above:
During May 1990 United Parcel Services (UPS) took the decision to re-engine its cargo fleet with Rolls-Royce Tay 651-54 engines. All three inlets are noticeably bigger on the Tay-powered aircraft, and the centre one has been raised well clear of the fuselage. *Rolls-Royce*

Advanced passenger model. The new aircraft was fitted with a reinforced cabin floor, a roller-conveyor system, and a 707-style cargo door in the port side of the forward fuselage: all passenger windows were omitted, as were most of the cabin amenities and emergency exits (basic facilities were retained for the three-man flight crew). The fuselage was equipped to carry up to 11 standard cargo containers with a combined weight of just over 60,000lb. The 16,000lb-thrust JT8D-17A powerplants were technically very similar to the (then) standard -17s, but several small design changes had been incorporated in the newer version, and these gave a 5% improvement in fuel efficiency. Fifteen 727-200Fs were ordered by the Memphis-based small-package carrier, Federal Express, but these were the only examples sold, and the whole 727 line was closed-down immediately after their completion. The first aircraft (N201FE) made its maiden flight on 28 April 1983, and the remaining 14 were manufactured on a combined 727/737 line at the fairly leisurely pace of just one per month; the final example (which was also the last of 1,832 727s built) was delivered to Federal Express as N217FE on 18 September 1984. Several dozen 200-series aircraft have been converted from passenger to cargo standard over the years, but the 15 727-200Fs were the only long-fuselage 727s fitted with a cargo door on the production line.

727UDF

During 1986 a single 727-100 (ex-OB-R-902 of the Peruvian airline, Faucett) was used as a test-bed and demonstrator for the General Electric Unducted Fan (UDF) programme. A proof-of-concept engine based on the military F404 core was installed on the starboard pylon of the 727, and a 75hr test programme was conducted between August 1986 and February 1987. A McDonnell-Douglas DC-9 (MD80) joined the programme in the spring of 1987, and was later shown at the 1988 Farnborough Air Display. The 727 was re-registered N32720 during the trials, and it flew for the first time from the Mojave Test Center in California on 21 August 1986. The aircraft was often referred to as the 727UDF, but this was not an 'official' Boeing designation, and there were never any plans to convert 727s to UDF power for commercial service.

727-300

The final throw of the 727 dice (at least as far as Boeing was concerned) was the projected 727-300 — a 220in stretch of the basic 727-200 fuselage with a modified wing, new four-wheel main undercarriage trucks, and wide-fan JT8D-217 engines. The wing included 747-style leading-edge flaps outboard, conventional slat section s inboard, and a much simpler system of double-slotted (as opposed to triple-slotted) trailing-edge flaps: the wing span was increased by 60in and the tailplane span by 40in. The aircraft was designed to carry 220 tourist-class passengers over a 2,000 mile stage length, with 10% better seat-mile costs than the 200-series. In the event, the -300 was 'de-emphasised' (Seattle-speak for cancelled) in 1975, when the company's attention switched to a project that later became the 757.

Engine Changes

727QF

During May 1990 the US small-package carrier United Parcel Services (UPS) took the bold decision to re-engine its entire fleet of cargo-equipped 727-100s with the Rolls-Royce Tay 651-54 — a modern, high by-pass ratio turbofan, providing 15,100lb thrust for take-off (compared with only 14,000lb for the original JT8D-7s). The new engines offered a 12% reduction in fuel consumption, lower maintenance costs, and an easy compliance with Stage 3 of the FAR Part 36 noise regulations. The conversion would also add considerable resale value to the aircraft, extending their operational lives well into the next century. In addition to the engine change, each cockpit was upgraded to include electronic instrumentation manufactured by Rockwell-Collins and Smiths Industries. The modification contract — which included 40 firm orders and 40 options — was awarded to the Dee Howard organisation, based at San Antonio in Texas.

The programme required the replacement of all three JT8Ds, and involved a substantial redesign of the rear fuselage. An enlarged S-duct was needed to cope with the greater mass-flow of the Tay, and the central intake had to be raised well clear of the fuselage to avoid the turbulent boundary layer at high angles of attack. The chord of the side-engine struts was increased, and their upper profile was flattened slightly; the engines themselves were canted downwards and outwards by about 1.5° to bring the thrust-line closer to the centreline of the aircraft. Aerodynamic strakes were added to the new nacelles and to both sides of the rear fuselage, and the side-engines only were fitted with Dee Howard-designed TR6000 thrust reversers. The centre engine was not equipped with a reverser, and is simply throttled back for landing.

The first Tay-powered aircraft flew on 18 April 1992. The type gained its FAA Certificate in November that year, and the first two were handed over to UPS in December. Since then, the programme has maintained steady progress, and at the time of writing virtually all of the first 40 had been delivered; no announcement has been made regarding the 40 options. The modifications take each airframe out of service for about three months, and completed 'production' examples are dubbed 727QF (Quiet Freighter) by UPS, Dee Howard and Rolls-Royce — although the designation has not been adopted by Boeing.

The Valsan answer

Another approach to fitting quieter engines (this time to the longer-fuselage 727-200) was adopted by Valsan Partners of New York. To avoid structural changes to the tail, the centre JT8D-17 (16,000lb thrust) remained in situ and was operated at low power settings for take-off and landing; it was also fitted with an acoustically-treated tailpipe and nozzle. The two outer engines only were replaced with much more modern, large fan, JT8D-217s — which were quieter in themselves, and developed about 20,000lb thrust for take-off; these were fitted into special acoustic nacelles manufactured by Rohr Industries. A Supplementary Type Certificate was issued for the aircraft in October 1988, and a Danish charter carrier ordered 15 conversions. The US Federal Aviation Administration (FAA) granted a full Stage 3 noise certificate in January 1989. At one time Valsan claimed to have 68 firm orders for the conversion, but the company eventually ceased trading in 1994 after completing only 22.

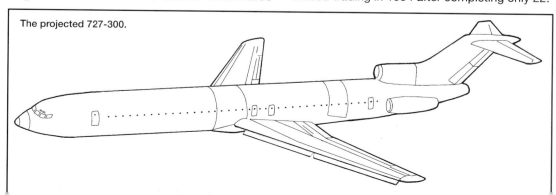

The projected 727-300.

Casualties

A chronological list of aircraft accidents will always give a misleading impression of the safety factors built into a successful commercial airliner, but there is no other way of recording these inevitable losses. To put the following list in context, it should be remembered that 1,832 727s were built between 1963 and 1984, and only 54 of these have been violently destroyed during nearly 30 years of day-to-day airline service: none of the accidents have been attributed to any weakness in the design of the aircraft or its systems, although sub-standard maintenance may have been a contributing factor on two or three occasions. Several aircraft have been destroyed in collisions or blown-up by terrorists, and one has been deliberately shot down, but by far the biggest group are those which were flown into high ground while operating within 50 miles of their destination airport.

The information shown includes (from left to right): the factory line number of the aircraft concerned; its construction number; the registration being carried at the time of the accident; the operator; and the date of the accident. Wherever possible, an explanation of the circumstances and causes are also given.

| 146 | 18328 | N7036U | United AL | 16 Aug 65 |

Crashed into Lake Michigan while approaching Chicago O'Hare in darkness, inbound from New York's La Guardia Airport. No survivors among the 24 passengers and six crew. The aircraft had been cleared by ATC from 16,000ft down to 6,000ft, but it continued descending until the point of impact. The wreckage was in deep water, and only two thirds had been recovered after three months. The Flight Data Recorder (FDR) was not found. The National Transportation Safety Board (NTSB) report was issued in January 1968, but the cause of the accident could not be positively determined. No evidence could be found of sabotage, engine problems, or systems malfunction, and there were no emergency calls from the crew. Everything seemed to be operating normally until the aircraft entered the water. Possible misreading of the altimeter, but this was conjecture.

| 153 | 18901 | N1996 | American AL | 8 Nov 65 |

Struck a wooded hillside in heavy rain, 1.5 miles from Greater Cincinnati Airport, Ohio – inbound from La Guardia, New York. Impact in darkness, at 19.02hr local time. Four survivors (three passengers and one stewardess) among the 56 passengers and six crew on board. NTSB report attributed the accident to pilot error — failure to monitor altimeters during the approach. The crash site was in a valley, some 225ft below the airport elevation, and yet the crew seemed totally unaware of their dangerously low altitude and rate of continued descent. The report noted the similarity in terms of pilot judgement between this and the Lake Michigan accident.

| 130 | 18322 | N7030U | United AL | 11 Nov 65 |

Main undercarriage units collapsed after heavy landing at Salt Lake City. Night approach, with a sink-rate of 2,000ft/min recorded by the FDR, subjecting the airframe to vertical deceleration forces of 4.7g. Touched down 365ft short of the runway. The impact caused the undercarriage legs to collapse inwards, which ruptured the aluminium fuel lines. Kerosene mist ignited by sparks, either from broken electrical generator leads or from the structure scraping along the runway. Fire spread rapidly into the fuselage, which was largely intact when it came to rest. All six crew survived, but 43 of the 83 passengers perished, most of them from the combined effects of smoke inhalation and fire. The official report blamed the crew for failing to monitor their sink rate, but questions were already being asked about the safety of the 727 — in particular, why three virtually brand-new aircraft should crash in such similar circumstances. The Federal Aviation Authority (FAA) later insisted that the aircraft's undercarriage be modified to prevent it collapsing into the fuselage. The generator leads also had to be moved to a less vulnerable position, and the aluminium fuel lines had to be replaced by a much stronger, more flexible material. The Seattle production-specifications were quickly changed, and nearly 300 modification kits were supplied to existing operators. This accident was also a watershed in overall safety terms, because everyone on board should have survived. The investigation triggered a search for less-combustible cabin materials, and led to much more stringent evacuation standards for all passenger-carrying aircraft. Both of these are now fully enshrined in FAA and CAA certification requirements.

| 126 | 18822 | JA8302 | All Nippon | 4 Feb 66 |

The fourth 727 night-approach crash in less than six months. The aircraft fell into Tokyo Bay at 19.00hr local time while inbound to Tokyo International from Chitose, on the island of Hokkaido. The weather was reported fine and clear, and there were no indications from the crew of any pre-crash problems. Impact occurred about 12 miles from the airport, killing all 126 passengers and seven crew — at that time the heaviest loss of life in the world for any crash involving just one aircraft (a mid-air collision in the USA had claimed 136 lives in December 1960). The flight-crew was again blamed for letting the rate of descent get out of control, but before the investigation was completed, the FAA brought all 727 users together to discuss the general operation of the aircraft. Out of this meeting came a new recognition of the potential dangers of flying slow approaches at flight-idle thrust settings. Because of its remarkable high-lift system the aircraft could cope with this and remain under full control, but if the sink-rate was allowed to increase rapidly, it would take too long to spool-up the engines in order to check the descent. New training and operational requirements for the 727 were introduced

Above:
N317PA crashed in communist-controlled East Berlin at the height of the Cold War. Much of the wreckage seems to have been spirited away to research institutes in Moscow, which made a normal investigation of the accident almost impossible.

by the FAA. These included the co-pilot monitoring speed and altitude; and calling these out to the command pilot at regular intervals during all visual approaches.

221 18995 N317PA Pan American 15 Nov 66

Cargo flight. Crashed on approach to Tegal Airport in West Berlin, inbound from Frankfurt. Impact occurred at 01.42hr local time, about 10 miles southwest of the aircraft's destination, in what was then the Soviet-controlled eastern sector of the city. Visibility was bad, with ⁸/₈ cloud above 600ft and drifting snowstorms in the area. All three crew were killed. Requests for access to the crash site were refused by Soviet officials, and the investigators had to work on wreckage returned by truck. The flight data and cockpit voice recorders were both missing, together with several other high-value components and systems — all of which were probably stolen for dissection in Moscow (a common problem in those days). The cause of the accident could not be positively determined, but the weather was clearly a major factor.

004   18295   N68650 Piedmont AL   19 Jul 67

One of the 727 development aircraft, but in airline service at the time of the accident: mid-air collision with Cessna 310 (N31215) over North Carolina. Carrying 74 passengers and a crew of five, the 727 had just taken-off from Asheville, and was in a climbing turn at 4,000ft. The Cessna was inbound to the same airfield, carrying a pilot and two passengers. The aircraft hit each other virtually head-on in cloud, and both crashed in relatively open country. There were no survivors. The NTSB report was issued in July 1968, but it was impossible to determine fully the cause of the accident. The ATC instructions to the Cessna were certainly ambiguous with hindsight, but they were accepted without any questions being raised. As a result, the Cessna pilot made incorrect assumptions, which caused him to stray into the 727's assigned airspace.

339 19175   B-1018 Civil Air Transport
16 Feb 68

Crash-landed six miles short of Taipei (Formosa) International Airport after a technically-unauthorised pilot took the controls. This was a night flight, inbound from Hong Kong with 52 passengers and 11 crew on board. The recognised captain allowed a management pilot to have his seat for the landing. This 'reserve' captain — who was qualified to fly the 727, but not authorised to do so on this particular flight — failed to monitor both the altitude and the sink rate. The aircraft broke up and caught fire after touching down in open country. Three crew members and 18 passengers were killed, and all the survivors were injured in some way, six of them seriously. A report from the Nationalist Chinese Air Force was issued very quickly (only three weeks after the accident), claiming negligence as the primary cause. The pilots involved — both Americans — were immediately charged with manslaughter, but they were acquitted at their trial in January 1969.

416 19200   N7425U United AL   21 Mar 68

Aborted take-off on night cargo service from Chicago O'Hare. Five seconds after brake release the 'take-off configuration' warning horn sounded, indicating a problem with flaps, spoilers, APU exhaust door, or tailplane trim. Rather than abandon their take-off, the crew attempted to trace the problem while still accelerating. Rotation and lift-off was achieved, but the aircraft would not climb away, and the stick-shaker operated to indicate an impending stall. The captain elected to put the aircraft back on the runway, but it veered off and struck a drainage ditch, which sheared-off the undercarriage. The aircraft then broke up and caught fire, and the three crew escaped through the cockpit windows. It was later established that the flaps were set at 2° instead of the required 5°.

540 19690 YA-FAR Ariana Afghan AL 5 Jan 69

Inbound to Gatwick on a scheduled flight from Kabul, via Frankfurt. Very poor visibility (100m RVR) in freezing fog, in the early hours of the morning. Although the visibility was technically below the required minimum, the captain elected to try an automatic approach, before a possible diversion to Heathrow. The flaps were incorrectly set when the aircraft intercepted the glide path, which resulted in an immediate 'landing configuration' warning. This was somehow interpreted as a system fault, and the autopilot was disconnected, leaving the aircraft under manual control. Flap was increased from 15° to 30°, which rapidly steepened the rate of descent. By the time the captain realised he was below the glidepath, it was too late. He initiated an overshoot from about 200ft, but the aircraft hit trees and a house 1.5 miles from the threshold, broke up and caught fire. The flight crew of three and 11 passengers survived, but 45 passengers and five cabin crew were killed: two people from the house also perished, and one was seriously injured. The Board of Trade accident investigators blamed the flight crew, but they also heavily criticised a separate BoT department for its withdrawal of precision approach radar facilities at Gatwick: this had been done some months before the crash as part of a cost-cutting exercise, but had it been operational that night it would have provided the crew with a much earlier warning of glidepath deviation.

631 19891 N7434U United AL 18 Jan 69

Crashed into the sea at night, four minutes after take-off from Los Angeles International Airport. On departure, the No 3 electrical generator was unserviceable — a condition known to the crew and acceptable to the flight dispatcher. Less than two minutes after take-off a fire warning for No 1 engine sounded and the powerplant was quite properly shut down, leaving the aircraft with only one generator to handle the entire electrical load. The captain reported the problem to the tower, and elected to return to the airport. The heavy load on the No 2 generator then caused it, too, to trip off line, and for some reason the emergency back-up system did not operate — either through technical failure, or because it was never activated by the crew. This train of events left the aircraft with a total loss of electrical power, which disabled all the flight deck attitude instruments. In cloud and darkness, the crew suffered a complete loss of attitude orientation at about 2,500ft, and the aircraft fell into Santa Monica Bay 11.3 miles from the airport. The wreckage sank in 1,000ft of water, but the FDR and CVR were recovered intact. These later revealed that the aircraft had impacted at a very steep angle and high speed, killing all 32 passengers and six crew.

532 19812 CC-CAQ LAN-Chile 28 Apr 69

Forced landing on open farmland some 15 miles north of Colina, Chile, inbound to Santiago on a scheduled flight from Buenos Aires. The aircraft was destroyed, but no details were circulated by the Chilean investigators. The number of occupants was unknown, but the accident was reported as non-fatal. It had been suggested that the aircraft ran out of fuel, but this was never confirmed.

355 19256 XA-SEL Mexicana 4 Jun 69

On approach to Monterrey in Northern Mexico, inbound on a scheduled flight from Mexico City with 72 passengers and seven crew on board. The aircraft hit high ground in a severe thunderstorm, some miles from its intended destination. There were no survivors. No details of causes, but poor navigation and windshear are obvious possibilities.

331 19255 XA-SEJ Mexicana 21 Sep 69

Crashed into Lake Texcoco on approach to Mexico City, inbound from Chicago. Crash occurred during the late evening, and no indication was given of any problem prior to impact. Of the 111 passengers and seven crew on board, 89 passengers and two crew survived, which suggests a controlled 'landing' in shallow water. The FDR and CVR both survived in readable condition, but the full accident report has not been widely published.

717 20240 N8790R Trans Caribbean AW 28 Dec 70

Overran after touch-down on St Thomas, one of the US Virgin Islands. The undercarriage sheared off, and the aircraft broke into several large pieces. Two passengers were killed in the ensuing fire, but 44 passengers and all seven crew managed to escape. Misjudged approach to a short (4,600ft) runway.

788 20436 JA8329 All Nippon 30 Jul 71

Destroyed in mid-air collision with JASDF F-86F Sabre — one of a pair on a training flight from Matsushima AB. The airliner was heading south towards Tokyo International, nearing the end of a scheduled flight from Sapporo, on the island of Hokkaido. The Sabres strayed into the 727's assigned airspace and the collision occurred about 385 miles north of Tokyo. Both aircraft fell into open country, killing all 155 passengers and seven crew aboard the 727: the fighter pilot was saved by his parachute. As a direct result of the accident, the C-in-C of the Air Staff resigned, together with the civilian Director General of the Self Defence Forces. Disciplinary action was taken against several staff officers, including the student pilot and his Flight leader, both of whom served long prison sentences for involuntary manslaughter. Aviation law in Japan was later revised to restrict severely all military activity in assigned airways.

287 19304 N2969G Alaska AL 4 Sep 71

Flew into a cliff face at 2,500ft while descending towards Juneau, Alaska, at the end of a scheduled flight from Anchorage. All 104 passengers and seven crew were killed — at the time, the worst single-aircraft disaster in US history. The airfield at Juneau was very poorly equipped to receive inbound aircraft over mountainous terrain: a localiser was operational, but there was no glideslope or DME, so height information had to be derived via bearings from a VOR beacon. The pilot was cleared to cross an intersection 'at or below 9,000ft', and the published chart for the area shows a safety height of 6,500ft initially, reducing to 5,000ft after crossing. The safety guidelines appear to have been disregarded, because the aircraft had strayed well below 3,000ft at the time of impact. The pilots were blamed for failing to monitor their height and position accurately, but the report was highly critical of the equipment standards at Juneau.

650 20244 5A-DAH Libyan Arab AL 21 Feb 73

Shot down over Sinai by two Israeli AF F-4Es. The aircraft was operating a scheduled Tripoli-Benghazi-Cairo service, and was inbound to Cairo when it strayed east of the Suez Canal, into airspace controlled by Israel. The Air France captain was on secondment to Libyan Arab as part of a technical assistance programme: the co-pilot was a Libyan national who could neither speak nor understand French. The aircraft was due to land at Cairo at 14.05hr local time, and was basically on time. It was equipped with twin VORs, DMEs and ADFs, all of which appeared to be serviceable. The primary ground aids for the area (Qarun and Cairo VORs) were both operating satisfactorily, but the Cairo NDB was not radiating properly at the relevant time. Most significantly, the Cairo approach surveillance radar had not been working for several years, so all ATC instructions were given to the aircraft on the basis of accurate positional reports from the crew. In fact the aircraft was lost, but the crew believed they were still on track, and reported this to Cairo.

As a result of this error, new heading instructions given by Cairo put the 727 on a direct course for the Israeli air base at Bir Gifgafa: at the same time, it was cleared to descend from FL290 to FL140, and then cleared again to 4,000ft. Shortly after these instructions were received, the 727 captain realised he was off track, and asked Cairo for a radar fix. This could only be obtained from military defence radars, but seeking permission via land line inevitably took time. Meanwhile, the descending airliner was spotted by Israeli radars, and two F-4Es were scrambled to intercept.

As the airliner descended through 6,000ft, the co-pilot saw what he thought were 'four MiGs behind us'. It was assumed that these were Egyptian AF aircraft, and after advising Cairo, the 727 turned left and levelled-off at about 6,000ft. The Phantoms were not equipped with VHF radios and could not talk directly to the 727, but one of them approached to within 12m of the cockpit, and its pilot pointed downwards. It then pulled ahead and rocked its wings, indicating that the 727 should follow. At that point Cairo ATC reported that a radar fix was being attempted, and asked the 727 to climb to 10,000ft because the minimum safe altitude in the area was 8,000ft.

A few seconds after the climb was initiated, both pilots saw a burst of tracer fire ahead of them, and began once more to descend. The fighters again closed-in on the 727, making more signalling movements — which were apparently misunderstood, because little was done to alter course or altitude. Three short bursts of cannon fire were then directed at

the starboard wingtip of the 727, and this was immediately reported to Cairo — only then, did the co-pilot identify the aggressors as Israeli. The next burst of gunfire was much more serious: it ripped into the starboard wing root, penetrating the main wheel bay to damage hydraulic systems and fuel tanks. This left the airliner virtually crippled. Several rounds hit the starboard and centre engines, and the starboard elevator horn and mass balance were sheared-off. A small fire appeared to break out in the starboard wing. At that time the 727 was at 5,000ft, and it continued to descend at nearly 2,000ft/min until it was seen by the Israeli pilots to attempt a flapless, wheels-up landing in open country. Considering that he was completely devoid of all electrical and hydraulic power for the last 105sec of flight, the pilot did remarkably well to 'land' at all.

Unfortunately, the aircraft broke up and caught fire during the post-impact slide, killing 110 of the 113 people on board. The Israeli Government later 'justified' its action by claiming that the Arab 727 had ignored repeated warnings, and was therefore assumed to be on a hostile mission.

516 19819 XV-NJC Air Vietnam 15 Sep 74

Blown-up in the air by politically motivated hijacker. Scheduled service between Singapore and Da Nang, with 68 passengers and eight crew on board. The aircraft was diverted to Phan Rang, but was destroyed without warning as it approached the airfield. Some reports mention three survivors, but this seems unlikely in a mid-air explosion and crash from flying speed.

777 20296 N274US Northwest AL 1 Dec 74

Crashed into Bear Mountain National Park, outbound from New York's La Guardia Airport. Positioning flight to Buffalo, with only three crew on board. Information retrieved from the FDR confirmed that the aircraft reached 24,800ft before it entered a steep descent — which at one point exceeded 17,000ft/min. At 20,000ft the crew reported they were out of control, and at 12,000ft they said they were in an irretrievable stall. The aircraft spiralled down in a basically flat attitude, turning slowly to the right until it hit the ground about 20° nose down: the port tailplane failed upwards some seconds before impact. All three occupants were killed. The NTSB investigation discovered that the crew failed to switch on the pitot heaters before departure — something that should have been corrected as part of the pre-flight call-and-response check list. This condition allowed ice to build up around both pressure heads, which gradually generated spurius instrument readings. These were misinterpreted on the flightdeck and the resulting mismanagement of the situation put the aircraft into its terminal descent.

791 20306 N54328 Trans World AL 1 Dec 74

Scheduled flight from Indianapolis to Washington National Airport, with 85 passengers and seven crew on board. Because high winds and heavy rain were disrupting traffic at National, the aircraft was unexpectedly diverted to Washington Dulles. It crashed into a wooded hillside in the Blue Ridge Mountains, about 40 miles northwest of its new destination: there were no survivors. Tapes from the CVR revealed that the captain misinterpreted the ATC instruction '...you are cleared to approach...'. All charts for the impact area showed a minimum safe altitude of 3,400ft but the crew were flying on instruments, and assumed that their clearance gave them radar protection for an unrestricted descent to 1,800ft — which was the safety height at the next intersection. The NTSB report blamed the crew for disregarding published safety heights, but two out of the five inspectors took a different view, and blamed ATC for not giving specific height restrictions: the dissenters felt that the flight was accepted as a radar arrival, and was therefore entitled to expect terrain clearance information. The law was later changed in the United States, making it illegal for a pilot to descend below published safety heights unless he receives a specific clearance to do so.

837	20443	N8845E Eastern AL	24 Jun 75

On final approach to runway 22L at Kennedy Airport, New York, inbound from New Orleans with 116 passengers and seven crew on board. The area to the west and northwest of the airport was affected by heavy thunderstorms, with some of the bigger clouds rising to 50,000ft. The 727 captain heard several aircraft ahead of him reporting severe turbulence and windshear problems to ATC, and as a precaution, decided to approach at 140kt — 10kt faster than normal. This higher speed was maintained fairly evenly down to 300ft, but at that height the FDR revealed an almost instantaneous drop to 122kt — well below the datum approach speed. Full take-off thrust was applied almost immediately, but the aircraft continued to lose speed and sink rapidly, and just 1.5sec after the throttles were moved it hit the first of several approach-lighting towers. Fire broke out soon after impact, and the aircraft skidded to a halt on Rockaway Boulevard — a major highway just outside the airport boundary. No-one on the ground was killed, but only nine of the aircraft occupants survived. The report confirmed that weather conditions were the primary cause of the crash, but the ATC cell was heavily criticised for continuing to use the runway after several crews had reported a severe weather hazard.

608	19798	N88777 Continental AL	7 Aug 75

On take-off from Stapleton International at Denver, Colorado, in good visibility but with a severe thunderstorm in the area. Just after lift-off the aircraft encountered a powerful windshear and was unable to maintain flying speed: it sank back onto the runway with its undercarriage partially retracted, and skidded for about 500ft before coming to rest. A fire developed in the tail section, but this was quickly dealt with by the airport rescue services. There were no fatalities among the 124 passengers and seven crew, but 15 people were seriously injured. The NTSB report blamed freak weather conditions for the crash. The aircraft was effectively written-off, but the hull was later sold to American Jet Industries for spares.

439	19525	HK-1272	Avianca	30 Sep 75

Few details available. Known to have crashed on landing at Barranquilla, Colombia, after reporting an emergency during a non-scheduled cargo flight from Bogata to Miami. The crew of four (pilot, co-pilot, flight engineer and loadmaster) were all killed.

124	18821	N124AS	Alaska AL	5 Apr 76

Crashed while landing at Ketchikan, Alaska, at the end of a scheduled domestic flight from Anchorage, with 50 passengers and seven crew on board. Misjudged approach. Touched-down a long way beyond the threshold, overran the end of the runway and fell into a ravine: the aircraft was badly damaged, but most of the occupants escaped before fire took hold. One passenger killed, five passengers and five crew injured.

499	19837	N1963	American AL	27 Apr 76

Crashed while landing on St Thomas in the US Virgin Islands, after a scheduled flight from Newport, Rhode Island: the occupants included 81 passengers and seven crew. The approach was flown with only 30° of flap instead of the usual 40°, which put the aircraft over the threshold at least 10kt faster than normal reference speed. The flare then took longer than expected, and windshear problems caused an unplanned 'float' which delayed touchdown until about 3,000ft along the 4,900ft runway. The captain initially decided to go round again, but 5sec after moving the throttles he mistakenly believed that the engines were not responding. He then tried to abandon the rolling take-off and stop the aircraft using only the wheel brakes: thrust reversers and spoilers were not deployed. The aircraft overran at high speed, tore off a wing by colliding with an embankment, and finally came to rest straddling a filling station outside the airport boundary. The ensuing fire killed 37 and injured 38 of those on board. One person on the ground was also injured. The NTSB report blamed the captain for attempting to take-off and go round again; had he applied all the available braking (wheel brakes, reverse thrust and spoilers) at the moment of touchdown, the aircraft would have come to rest a good deal less violently, and may even have stopped on the runway without suffering significant damage.

1087	20982	TC-JBH	Turk Hava Yollari	19 Sep 76

Crashed into Mount Karatepe, eight miles south of Isparta, nearing the end of a flight from Istanbul to Antalya. At least 12min before his ETA, the captain told Antalya tower that he could see the runway lights ahead, and was beginning his decent. The tower then warned him that he was still some 60 miles away from the airfield, and it was quite impossible to see the lights from his position. The pilot acknowledged the warning and started to climb, but the aircraft hit the top of the mountain just a few seconds later. All 147 passengers and eight crew perished. Subsequent reports in a Turkish newspaper suggested that the 'runway' seen by the crew was actually the main street through Isparta, which is very wide and brightly lit, and runs dead straight through the town for nearly two miles.

1096	20972	CS-TBR	TAP Air Portugal	19 Nov 77

Crashed on landing at Madeira Funchal, with the loss of 123 passengers and six crew. The visibility was bad (but within legal limits) and the crew made three separate approaches using a non-directional beacon for guidance. On the first attempt there was no visual contact at decision height, and on the second, contact was made and then lost again. On the third attempt, the aircraft crossed the threshold at about 50ft, but refused to settle on the runway due to a severe updraft. Touchdown was finally achieved some way beyond the threshold, but the aircraft began to aquaplane immediately and failed to decelerate. Despite the use of wheel brakes, spoilers and full-power reverse thrust, the 727 overran the far end of the 5,250ft runway at nearly 120kt, and crashed onto the beach beyond, exploding on impact. Pilot misjudgement was cited as the primary cause of the accident, but tiredness could have been a significant contributing factor. Through no fault of their own, the crew had been subjected to delays on each of the three sectors flown that day, which resulted in a total duty time of 12hr 45min.

553   19464   N4744   National AL   8 May 78

On approach to Pensacola, Florida, after a scheduled flight from Mobile, Alabama, with 52 passengers and six crew on board. Visibility was very poor, with a cloud-base down to 400ft – which was below the approved minimum for the approach. The crew allowed the aircraft to drift way below the required flight path, which triggered the GPWS to sound its 'pull-up' warning. The captain assumed that this referred to excessive sink-rate rather than low altitude, and continued to descend at a slightly reduced rate. The aircraft broke out of cloud and effectively 'landed' in shallow water, at a point where it should have been established on finals, and still at 1,250ft. Three passengers died in the accident, and one of the crew was seriously injured.

589 19688   N533PS   Pacific Southwest AL
25 Sep 78

Mid-air collision with Cessna 172 (N7711G) near San Diego International Airport (Lindbergh Field), killing a total of 137 people from the two aircraft, and a further seven on the ground. At the time, this was the highest death toll of any aircraft accident in the US. The 727 was inbound to San Diego, at the end of a scheduled trip from Sacramento and Los Angeles; the Cessna was on an instrument training flight from nearby Montgomery Field, with two experienced commercial pilots on board. The impact occurred three miles northeast of Lindbergh, while the 727 was turning finals prior to an ILS approach to runway 27; the Cessna was due to line up for an identical approach. Both aircraft were aware of each other, but the 727 captain had been given the responsibility of maintaining visual separation — first because he was the larger aircraft, and second because he was preparing to overtake the Cessna. The trainer was in sight from the 727 until the final turn was initiated: at that point both aircraft were flying directly into brilliant sunlight, which was diffused and flared by the early morning haze. The airliner crew lost visual contact with the Cessna for a few seconds, but this fact was not reported to Lindbergh tower. At 09.02hr local time, the Cessna was flying at about 105kt when it was hit from behind by the starboard wing of the 727. Both aircraft broke-up in the air, and wreckage fell on the suburbs of San Diego, destroying a number of houses. After examining all the flight records, the investigating board could do little else but blame the 727 captain for failing to maintain the required visual separation, but the ATC system was strongly criticised for allowing two such dissimilar aircraft to use visual procedures when they were on such obviously conflicting tracks.

1061   20886 JY-ADU Alia – Royal Jordanian AL
14 Mar 79

Few details available, but known to have crashed in heavy thunderstorms while attempting to land at Doha, in Qatar. The aircraft was on a scheduled flight with 49 passengers and 15 company employees on board — eight of whom were on a positioning flight. Three crew members and 42 passengers are known to have perished. Possible windshear?

537 19817   EP-IRD   Iran Air   21 Jan 80

Flew into high ground while approaching Tehran's Mehrabad Airport. Scheduled service with 120 passengers and eight crew on board – all of whom perished. The aircraft should have been under positive radar control throughout this approach, but an ATC strike had ended just a few hours earlier and some of the equipment was still not fully operational. The captain reported that he was flying through heavy snowstorms, and a few seconds later the aircraft hit a rocky outcrop near Lashgarak, some 18 miles north of the airport.

297 19111   PT-TYS   Transbrasil 12 Apr 80

Scheduled domestic flight from Sao Paulo, to Floriapolis in southern Brazil, carrying 50 passengers and eight crew. As far as is known, no faults or emergencies were called, but the approach to Floriapolis was flown far too low, and apparently off course. There were heavy thunderstorms in the area, and the aircraft hit a wooded hillside some 300ft below the summit. Remarkably, four passengers survived the impact.

288 19279   G-BDAN   Dan Air   25 Apr 80

While holding to land at Los Rodeos Airport on the island of Tenerife, the aircraft flew into cloud-covered mountains some 12 miles south of the runway: none of the 138 passengers and eight crew survived the impact. The initial approach to Tenerife airspace was entirely normal, and permission was given for a procedural IFR let-down to runway 12. This plan was quickly rescinded by ATC, and the 727 was asked to adopt a non-standard holding pattern while an Iberia F.27 landed. The wording of the ATC instruction was ambiguous, and the holding pattern itself was not published on aeronautical charts for the area. The 727 captain was given only about 50secs to initiate the procedure, but he accepted it without question, and began what he understood to be the required turn — a turn that would take him into an area where the minimum safe altitude was 14,500ft. At that time he was flying at 6,000ft, and had just been cleared to descend to 5,000ft. There was no radar coverage in the area. Less than two minutes after accepting the hold, the aircraft hit the side of a mountain at 5,700ft. The Spanish report on the accident admitted 'certain deficiencies' in the ATC system, but these were generally played-down, and the enquiry went on to blame the Dan Air crew — basically for their lack of professionalism and positional awareness. The British AIB did not fully accept this conclusion, and in an unusual move, published its own very different findings. These agreed that the crew were partially responsible, in that they failed to seek clarification of a non-standard procedure, but several shortcoming in the ATC handling of the flight were highlighted as major contributory factors.

1282 21347 PP-SRK VASP 8 Jun 82

On approach to Pinto Martins Airport, Fortaleza, at the end of a scheduled service from Sao Paulo. Crashed into a hillside in the Serra da Pacatuba mountains, about five miles from the runway. Technical problems were apparently reported during the approach, which was being flown at 03.00hr local time, in wind and heavy rain. Impact occurred at about 2,500ft, killing all 128 passengers and seven crew.

518 19457 N4737 Pan American 9 Jul 82

Crashed into a housing estate two miles east of New Orleans, after taking-off in thundery weather. Eight people on the ground were killed, in addition to the 145 occupants of the aircraft. A violent windshear encountered 30sec after take-off caused the Pan Am aircraft to dive into the ground, and yet a Republic Airlines DC-9 which departed a few minutes earlier, experienced no problems at all. The 727 crew was aware of a windshear risk, but in view of the DC-9's trouble-free departure, their decision to take-off was fully understandable. They were entirely exonerated by the subsequent NTSB report, but the windshear detection system installed at New Orleans was criticised because it failed to pick up the destructive potential of the surrounding storm.

276 19171 EP-IRA Iran Air 7 Jan 83

Few details available, but noted as destroyed while taxiing at Tehran Airport. No reports of casualties.

1389 21603 TC-JBR Turk Hava Yollari 16 Jan 83

Crashed on landing at Ankara, after a scheduled domestic flight from Istanbul with 60 passengers and a crew of seven. Approached in fog and heavy snow, and touched down in soft ground 50m short of the runway, shearing off the undercarriage. The aircraft skidded, broke-up and caught fire, killing 47 of the passengers; all the crew survived. After analysis of the CVR and FDR tapes, a strong microburst-type windshear was cited as the major causal factor.

1019 20820 EC-CFJ Iberia 7 Dec 83

Taking-off in fog from runway 01 at Madrid/Barajas Airport, when it collided with an Aviaco DC-9 (EC-CGS). The 727 had been cleared for take-off, when the taxiing DC-9 became lost in the fog and inadvertently strayed onto the active runway. The Iberia captain lifted his aircraft early in an attempt to avoid the collision, but its rear fuselage slammed into the DC-9, which exploded on impact, killing all 42 occupants. The 727 fell back to the runway, broke up immediately, and started to burn while still sliding: of the 93 people on board, 49 passengers and one member of the crew were killed, and many more were seriously injured. The subsequent report blamed the Aviaco crew for their lack of attention in difficult conditions.

284 19037 HK-1804 SAM-Colombia 15 Dec 83

No details confirmed, but understood to have been destroyed during a wheels-up landing on San Andres Island (?), Colombia. No casualty figures given. Even the date is disputed, with some reports suggesting 5 Oct 83,

1793 22556 N819EA Eastern AL 1 Jan 85

Crashed at 19,600ft while approaching La Paz in Bolivia, inbound from Paraguay, on a scheduled flight with 21 passengers and eight crew on board. There were no survivors. When the last position report was received at 19.37hr local time, everything appeared to be normal, with no indication of either mechanical or navigational problems. Just three minutes later, at 19.40hr, all clocks and watches on board stopped as the aircraft hit the cloud-covered slopes of Mount Illimani, a 21,000ft Andean peak some 40 miles southeast of La Paz.

1487 21777 EC-DDU Iberia 19 Feb 85

Flew into high ground while on a procedural approach to Bilbao, inbound from Madrid on a regular scheduled service. Crew allowed the aircraft to drift nearly a mile off track, and 1,000ft below the published let-down path. This put them in a position of descending through 3,500ft in a sector where the published safe altitude was 7,000ft. The aircraft was not equipped with a ground proximity warning system, and the mountains were obscured by cloud. The crash occurred shortly before 09.30hr local time, when the aircraft hit a 175ft television relay mast on top of Mount Oiz — a 3,300ft peak about 20 miles from Sondica. There were no survivors among the 141 passengers and seven crew.

1713 22271 JY-AFW Alia – Royal Jordanian AL 12 Jan 85

Aircraft seized by terrorists at Beirut Airport, and subsequently destroyed by explosive device and fire. No know casualties.

1748 22414 XA-MEM Mexicana 31 Mar 86

On climb-out from Mexico City, *en route* for the Pacific coastal resorts of Puerto Vallanta and Mazatlan. Scheduled domestic flight. The take-off at 08.50hr local time appeared to be quite normal, and 15min later the aircraft was on time and on track, and had just been cleared to continue its climb to 28,000ft. At 09.06hr the pilot reported a small explosion on board and problems with the pressurisation system; he was given immediate clearance to return to Mexico City. About 40sec later a second, much louder explosion occurred, and a fire started in the fuselage/port-wing intersection. The captain called a full emergency, but the aircraft began to break up at 15,000ft, and eventually crashed near the summit of the 7,800ft mountain, El Carbon. All 158 passengers and eight crew were killed. Witnesses on the ground confirmed the mid-air break-up, and several reported seeing smoke and flames as the aircraft descended. Suspicions immediately centred on a terrorist bomb, and various organisations tried to claim responsibility.

In fact, the investigation team later discovered that the initial explosion was caused by a tyre-burst inside the closed undercarriage bay. Debris from this ruptured several pipes and ducts, including one carrying fuel, and another carrying hot de-icing air bled straight from the engines. The misting fuel was ignited by the hot air (the second explosion), and the ensuing fire rapidly burned through the main fuselage structure, causing the tail section to fail under aerodynamic load. It seems certain that the port mainwheel brakes were binding throughout the long ground roll to the runway and during take-off. Under such circumstances, the hub would have been virtually incandescent when the undercarriage was retracted, and much of the trapped heat would have been absorbed by the tyres. As the external air pressure was reduced with altitude, the weakened tyre carcass failed with catastrophic results.

536	19728 N766AS	Alaska AL	9 Jun 87

After routine maintenance, two ground engineers were taxying the aircraft into position at Anchorage, when a wing struck one of the airport loading ramps. The impact ruptured one of the main fuel tanks, and spilt kerosene ignited, destroying both the aircraft and the ramp. The two engineers escaped, and there were no injuries to any of the bystanders.

| 1044 | 20930 TC-AKD | Talia Hava Yollari | |
| | | | 27 Feb 88 |

On a non-scheduled positioning flight from Istanbul to Kyrenia, Cyprus, with 15 company employees on board, including the flight crew of three. No fare-paying passengers carried. Approaching Kyrenia in difficult weather, the aircraft crashed into a mountain at Arapcoy, some 15 miles short of its destination. There were no survivors.

240	18999 HK-1716	Avianca	17 Mar 88

Flew into high ground in mist and rain, shortly after take-off from Cucuta, Colombia. The aircraft was on a scheduled domestic flight to the northwest coastal city of Cartagena, with 131 passengers and six crew on board — none of whom survived. Cucuta ATC reported losing contact with the aircraft at 13.14hr local time, just a few minutes after take-off. The wreckage was spotted some time later on a mountainside near Zulia, about 40 miles away from the departure runway.

199	18856 TI-LRC	LACSA	23 May 88

Aborted take-off after engine fire at San Jose Airport, Costa Rica. Aircraft slewed off the runway and was badly damaged, but there were no serious injuries among the 16 passengers and nine crew. Hull assessed as write-off.

992	20750 N473DA	Delta AL	31 Aug 88

On take-off from Dallas-Fort Worth, outbound on a scheduled service to Salt Lake City with 97 passengers and six crew on board. Departure was timed at 09.03hr local. From brakes-off the aircraft accelerated normally, rotated, and got airborne more or less as expected. Just after rotation, several compressor stalls occurred, and the aircraft was

reluctant to climb away despite the use of emergency power-settings on all three engines. At about 80ft the stick-shaker operated, and the aircraft stalled, falling back to earth about 30ft from the end of the runway. the undercarriage partially collapsed, causing the aircraft to turn and slide sideways for some distance. Fuel tanks were ruptured, and the fuselage broke in two just aft of the wing. The cabin section was destroyed by fire, but most of the passengers and all six crew managed to evacuate the aircraft safely; 15 passengers died in the accident. It was later established that the flaps were incorrectly set for take-off. The multiple compressor stalls were almost certainly caused by the centre engine reacting to an unusually steep angle of attack, as the pilot tried to haul the aircraft into the air. The 'take-off configuration' warning system failed to operate when the throttles were advanced, and this was a significant contributing factor to the accident. Subsequent spot-checks of similar systems on other aircraft (not just Boeings) revealed that a surprising number of them were either not working at all, or not working properly. More-frequent in-service checks were ordered by the FAA, and all US-registered airliners now have to carry a monitoring system to alert the pilot if the primary system fails.

| 597 | 19514 N88705 Transportes Aereos Nationales | |
| | | 21 Oct 89 |

Hit high ground during a procedural approach to the Honduran capital, Tegucigalpa, inbound from Managua in Nicaragua, with 135 passengers and seven crew on board. About 15 people survived the initial impact and fire, but at least seven died of their injuries later. The aircraft was on track when it encountered severe turbulence and high winds in cloud. The captain survived, and later told the investigating team that he was attempting to make a forced landing – perhaps as a result of powerful windshear forces. The aircraft was certainly under reasonable control when it touched-down, but the landing was made on soft, gently-rising ground, covered with bracken and scrub. The wreckage was widely scattered, but the forward cabin section remained relatively intact and clear of the fire.

272	19035 HK-1803	Avianca	27 Nov 89

Shortly after take-off from Bogota, Colombia, with 101 passengers and six crew on board; there were no survivors. The aircraft broke-up in the air while climbing, and crashed on a hillside some 15 mines south of the airport. Most of the wreckage fell in a very small area — indicating a near vertical descent — but a trail of minor debris extended back along the route for nearly two miles. Witnesses on the ground reported hearing explosions, and a terrorist group connected to the Medellin drug cartel later claimed to have blown-up the aircraft to kill five police informers.

760	20266 OB-1303	Faucett	11 Sep 90

Presumed crashed into the North Atlantic approximately 160 miles off Cape Race, on the Newfoundland coast of Canada. The aircraft was returning to Miami after a six-month wet lease arrangement with Air Malta. It was 30min overdue for a technical stop in Gander, when several commercial airliners picked up distress calls from the pilot. He reported that he was low on fuel and descending through 10,000ft, preparing to ditch. No position reports were given, and the aircraft was still outside Gander's radar range. A massive air and sea search was organised immediately, but there was nothing to confirm that the aircraft was on its intended track when it hit the sea. The search was called off about a week later, with no sign of the aircraft or its 15 occupants.

1173 21157 N278US   Northwest AL   3 Dec 90

In collision with Northwest AL DC-9 (N3313L) on the centre runway (21C/03C) at Detroit Metropolitan Airport, The DC-9 strayed onto the active runway in fog, while it was supposed to be on a parallel taxi track making its way down to the take-off point. The 727 had turned onto the runway, and was facing the DC-9 virtually head-on. As the 727 began to accelerate, the First Officer of the DC-9 was talking to the tower, trying to establish exactly where they were. Impact occurred at about 85kt, just as the 727 was preparing to rotate. The starboard wing of the 727 ripped into the DC-9's cabin and sheared-off its starboard engine, causing a fire which rapidly engulfed the stationary aircraft. The 727 did not catch fire, and all 156 people on board escaped with only a few minor injures. The DC-9 was carrying 39 passengers and five crew, eight of whom — including one cabin attendant — were killed, and a further 24 passengers were injured, some of them seriously. Poor crew co-ordination on the DC-9 was cited as the primary cause of the accident. The 727 captain was also criticised for attempting to take-off in visibility which was below his company's 400m minimum, and the ground controller was accused of contributing by not taking 'timely action' to avoid the collision.

1108 21050 5A-DIA   Libyan Arab AL
22 Dec 92

Inbound to Tripoli International after a scheduled domestic flight from Benghazi, carrying 147 passengers and 10 crew. Mid-air collision with a Libyan AF MiG-23 Flogger, which had reportedly just taken-off from the same airport. The 727 crashed about five miles east of Tripoli, killing everyone on board. Virtually no details were released by the Libyan Government.

217 18876 HK-2422   Sociedad Aeronautica
Medellin   19 May 93

On procedural approach to Medellin, Colombia, inbound on a scheduled service from Panama City. Few details are available at the time of writing, but understood to have crashed into mountains at 12,300ft, shortly after being cleared by ATC to descend to 12,000ft. Impact occurred 30 miles south of destination, and about 70 miles from the aircraft's last reported position. No survivors among the 126 passengers and six crew. Possible navigation error, or altimeter misreading?

Below:
This 727-100 of Iran Air (EP-IRA *Isfahan*) was destroyed in a mystery taxying accident at Tehran Airport — presumably by ground collision and/or fire (See page 77). *Hugh Newell*

Construction List

This list of individual 727 airframes is based on the original factory line numbers, and therefore shows the sequential order of construction. The recorded details refer to the original purchaser only, but a full service history can be obtained from John Roach and Tony Eastwood's excellent *Jet Airliner Production List*, published by the Aviation Hobby Shop, West Drayton, Middlesex.

Line No	Constrn No	Model No	First Operator	Delivery Registration	First flight
1	18293	22	United AL	N7001U	9 Feb 63
2	18464	22	Boeing	N72700	12 Mar 63
3	18294	22	United AL	N7002U	10 Apr 63
4	18295	22	All Nippon	N68650	22 May 63
5	18296	22	United AL	N7004U	12 Jun 63
6	18297	22	United AL	N7005U	28 Jun 63
7	18298	22	United AL	N7006U	16 Jul 63
8	18252	25	Eastern AL	N8101N	13 Aug 63
9	18299	22	United AL	N7007U	15 Aug 63
10	18300	22	United AL	N7008U	4 Sep 63
11	18253	25	Eastern AL	N8102N	10 Sep 63
12	18301	22	United AL	N7009U	18 Sep 63
13	18254	25	Eastern AL	N8103N	1 Oct 63
14	18255	25	Eastern AL	N8104N	9 Oct 63
15	18426	23	American AL	N1970	23 Oct 63
16	18256	25	Eastern AL	N8105N	7 Nov 63
17	18257	25	Eastern AL	N8106N	18 Nov 63
18	18427	23	American AL	N1971	27 Nov 63
19	18302	22	United AL	N7010U	10 Dec 63
20	18258	25	Eastern AL	N8107N	17 Dec 63
21	18428	23	American AL	N1972	27 Dec 63
22	18303	22	United AL	N7011U	31 Dec 63
23	18304	22	United AL	N7012U	10 Jan 64
24	18360	30	Lufthansa	D-ABIB	14 Jan 64
25	18259	25	Eastern AL	N8108N	24 Jan 64
26	18429	23	American AL	N1973	28 Jan 64
27	18305	22	United AL	N7013U	4 Feb 64
28	18361	30	Lufthansa	D-ABIC	4 Feb 64
29	18260	25	Eastern AL	N8109N	13 Feb 64
30	18261	25	Eastern AL	N8110N	17 Feb 64
31	18430	23	American AL	N1974	25 Feb 64
32	18431	23	American AL	N1975	27 Feb 64
33	18362	30	Lufthansa	D-ABID	5 Mar 64
34	18306	22	United AL	N7014U	10 Mar 64
35	18363	30	Lufthansa	D-ABIF	18 Mar 64
36	18569	31	TWA	N850TW	25 Mar 64
37	18364	30	Lufthansa	D-ABIG	27 Mar 64
38	18307	22	United AL	N7015U	1 Apr 64
39	18570	31	TWA	N851TW	7 Apr 64
40	18308	22	United AL	N7016U	9 Apr 64
41	18262	25	Eastern AL	N8111N	17 Apr 64
42	18571	31	TWA	N852TW	21 Apr 64
43	18432	23	American AL	N1976	21 Apr 64
44	18433	23	American AL	N1977	28 Apr 64
45	18263	25	Eastern AL	N8112N	5 May 64
46	18572	31	TWA	N853TW	6 May 64
47	18309	22	United AL	N7017U	15 May 64
48	18310	22	United AL	N7018U	21 May 64
49	18573	31	TWA	N854TW	22 May 64
50	18434	23	American AL	N1978	27 May 64
51	18435	23	American AL	N1979	3 Jun 64
52	18365	30	Lufthansa	D-ABIH	4 Jun 64
53	18264	25	Eastern AL	N8113N	11 Jun 64
54	18265	25	Eastern AL	N8114N	16 Jun 64
55	18311	22	United AL	N7019U	17 Jun 64
56	18574	31	TWA	N855TW	23 Jun 64
57	18575	31	TWA	N856TW	29 Jun 64
58	18436	23	American AL	N1980	30 Jun 64
59	18437	23	American AL	N1981	8 Jul 64
60	18312	22	United AL	N7020U	7 Jul 64
61	18266	25	Eastern AL	N8115N	16 Jul 64
62	18267	25	Eastern AL	N8116N	17 Jul 64
63	18576	31	TWA	N857TW	23 Jul 64
64	18577	31	TWA	N858TW	23 Jul 64
65	18438	23	American AL	N1982	4 Aug 64
66	18313	22	United AL	N7021U	30 Jul 64
67	18439	23	American AL	N1983	7 Aug 64
68	18578	31	TWA	N859TW	6 Aug 64
69	18440	23	American AL	N1984	14 Aug 64
70	18750	31	TWA	N849TW	15 Aug 64
71	18268	25	Eastern AL	N8117N	24 Aug 64
72	18741	76	TAA	VH-TJA	25 Aug 64
73	18314	22	United AL	N7022U	1 Sep 64
74	18269	25	Eastern AL	N8118N	3 Sep 64
75	18751	31	TWA	N848TW	9 Sep 64
76	18752	31	TWA	N847TW	10 Sep 64
77	18315	22	United AL	N7023U	17 Sep 64
78	18734	77	Ansett AL	VH-RME	21 Sep 64
79	18270	25	Eastern AL	N8119N	25 Sep 64
80	18316	22	United AL	N7024U	29 Sep 64
81	18742	76	TAA	VH-TJB	1 Oct 64
82	18271	25	Eastern AL	N8120N	5 Oct 64
83	18753	31	TWA	N846TW	8 Oct 64
84	18754	31	TWA	N845TW	13 Oct 64
85	18811	35	National AL	N4610	15 Oct 64
86	18744	77	Ansett AL	VH-RMF	18 Oct 64
87	18755	31	TWA	N844TW	22 Oct 64
88	18317	22	United AL	N7025U	27 Oct 64
89	18272	25	Eastern AL	N8121N	30 Oct 64
90	18797	51	NW Orient	N461US	3 Nov 64
91	18273	25	Eastern AL	N8122N	5 Nov 64
92	18812	35	National AL	N4611	11 Nov 64
93	18798	51	NW Orient	N462US	11 Nov 64
94	18813	35	National AL	N4612	18 Nov 64
95	18318	22	United AL	N7026U	23 Nov 64
96	18274	25	Eastern AL	N8123N	24 Nov 64
97	18441	23	American AL	N1985	25 Nov 64
98	18366	30	Lufthansa	D-ABIK	4 Dec 64
99	18794	78	BWIA	9Y-TCO	10 Dec 64
100	18814	35	National AL	N4613	8 Dec 64
101	18275	25	Eastern AL	N8124N	24 Dec 64
102	18799	51	NW Orient AL	N463US	17 Dec 64
103	18276	25	Eastern AL	N8125N	23 Dec 64
104	18795	78	BWIA	9Y-TCP	5 Jan 65
105	18442	23	American AL	N1986	31 Dec 64
106	18815	35	National AL	N4614	4 Jan 65
107	18277	25	Eastern AL	N8126N	12 Jan 65
108	18796	78	BWIA	9Y-TCQ	13 Jan 65
109	18367	30	Lufthansa	D-ABIL	19 Jan 65
110	18319	22	United AL	N7027U	19 Jan 65
111	18443	23	American AL	N1987	25 Jan 65
112	18816	35	National AL	N4615	25 Jan 65
113	18278	25	Eastern AL	N8127N	1 Feb 65
114	18444	23	American AL	N1988	2 Feb 65
115	18445	23	American AL	N1989	9 Feb 65
116	18800	51	NW Orient AL	N464US	5 Feb 65
117	18368	30	Lufthansa	D-ABIM	11 Feb 65
118	18817	35	National AL	N4616	16 Feb 65
119	18320	22	United AL	N7028U	17 Feb 65
120	18801	51	NW Orient AL	N465US	17 Feb 65
121	18279	25	Eastern AL	N8128N	1 Mar 65
122	18321	22	United AL	N7029U	26 Feb 65
123	18446	23	American AL	N1990	3 Mar 65
124	18821	81	All Nippon	JA8301	4 Mar 65
125	18369	30	Lufthansa	D-ABIN	10 Mar 65
126	18822	81	All Nippon	JA8302	11 Mar 65
127	18447	23	American AL	N1991	16 Mar 65
128	18802	51	NW Orient AL	N466US	17 Mar 65
129	18280	25	Eastern AL	N8129N	24 Mar 65
130	18322	22	United AL	N7030U	25 Mar 65
131	18448	23	American AL	N1992	26 Mar 65
132	18449	23	American AL	N1993	30 Mar 65

Line No	Constrn No	Model No	First Operator	Delivery Registration	First flight
133	18908	14	Pacific SW AL	N970PS	1 Apr 65
134	18370	30	Lufthansa	D-ABIP	17 Apr 65
135	18823	81	All Nippon	JA8303	9 Apr 65
136	18323	22	United AL	N7031U	12 Apr 65
137	18803	51	NW Orient AL	N467US	9 Apr 65
138	18092	31	TWA	N831TW	23 Apr 65
139	18324	22	United AL	N7032U	20 Apr 65
140	18450	23	American AL	N1994	27 Apr 65
141	18325	22	United AL	N7033U	29 Apr 65
142	18326	22	United AL	N7034U	5 May 65
143	18281	25	Eastern AL	N8130N	11 May 65
144	18327	22	United AL	N7035U	11 May 65
145	18371	30	Lufthansa	D-ABIQ	14 May 65
146	18328	22	United AL	N7036U	18 May 65
147	18903	31	TWA	N833TW	24 May 65
148	18892	44	SAA	ZS-DYM	25 May 65
149	18282	25	Eastern AL	N8131N	2 Jun 65
150	18909	14	PacificSW AL	N971PS	19 May 65
151	18900	23	American AL	N1995	4 Jun 65
152	18904	31	TWA	N839TW	10 Jun 65
153	18901	23	American AL	N1996	15 Jun 65
154	18329	22	United AL	N7037U	14 Jun 65
155	18283	25	Eastern AL	N8132N	21 Jun 65
156	18330	22	United AL	N7038U	22 Jun 65
157	18893	44	SAA	ZS-DYN	25 Jun 65
158	18331	22	United AL	N7039U	30 Jun 65
159	18910	14	Pacific SW AL	N972PS	23 Jun 65
160	18905	31	TWA	N840TW	2 Jul 65
161	18284	25	Eastern AL	N8133N	14 Jul 65
162	18804	51	NW Orient AL	N468US	13 Jul 65
163	18919	81	All Nippon	JA8305	19 Jul 65
164	18332	22	United AL	N7040U	20 Jul 65
165	18791	22	United AL	N7003U	23 Jul 65
166	18874	46	Japan AL	JA8307	9 Jul 65
167	18911	14	Pacific SW AL	N973PS	28 Jul 65
168	18894	44	SAA	ZS-DYO	2 Aug 65
169	18912	14	Pacific SW AL	N974PS	3 Aug 65
170	18843	76	TAA	VH-TJC	11 Aug 65
171	18844	77	Ansett AL	VH-RMD	6 Aug 65
172	18285	25	Eastern AL	N8134N	6 Aug 65
173	18895	44	SAA	ZS-DYP	13 Aug 65
174	18920	81	All Nippon	JA8306	16 Aug 65
175	18845	35	National AL	N4617	18 Aug 65
176	18906	31	TWA	N841TW	24 Aug 65
177	18848	22	United AL	N7041U	27 Aug 65
178	18849	22	United AL	N7042U	30 Aug 65
179	18805	51	NW Orient AL	N469US	31 Aug 65
180	18850	95	Northeast AL	N1631	2 Aug 65
181	18851	22	United AL	N7044U	7 Sep 65
182	18286	25	Eastern AL	N8135N	9 Sep 65
183	18846	35	National AL	N4618	10 Sep 65
184	18896	44	SAA	ZS-DYR	10 Sep 65
185	18933	30	Lufthansa	D-ABIR	11 Sep 65
186	18852	22	United AL	N7045U	12 Sep 65
187	18847	35	National AL	N4619	12 Sep 65
188	18806	51	NW Orient AL	N470US	14 Sep 65
189	18853	22	United AL	N7046U	14 Sep 65
190	18287	25	Eastern AL	N8136N	24 Sep 65
191	18854	22	United AL	N7047U	12 Oct 65
192	18288	25	Eastern AL	N8137N	19 Oct 65
193	18807	51	NW Orient AL	N471US	18 Oct 65
194	18289	25	Eastern AL	N8138N	25 Oct 65
195	18855	22	United AL	N7048U	22 Oct 65
196	19128	23	American AL	N1997	29 Oct 65
197	19129	23	American AL	N1998	3 Nov 65
198	18942	51	NW Orient AL	N472US	5 Nov 65
199	18856	22	United AL	N7049U	22 Oct 65
200	18857	22	United AL	N7050U	12 Nov 65
201	18290	25	Eastern AL	N8139N	16 Nov 65
202	18875	46	Japan AL	JA8308	15 Nov 65
203	18943	51	NW Orient AL	N473US	24 Nov 65
204	18291	25	Eastern AL	N8140N	29 Nov 65
205	18965	25	Eastern AL	N8141N	3 Dec 65
206	18992	21	Pan American	N314PA	6 Dec 65
207	18858	95	Northeast AL	N1632	9 Dec 65
208	18859	22	United AL	N7052U	4 Dec 65
209	18944	51	NW Orient AL	N474US	10 Dec 65
210	18860	22	United AL	N7053U	9 Dec 65
211	18897	51C	Boeing	N7270C	30 Dec 65
212	18861	22	United AL	N7054U	13 Dec 65
213	19130	23	American AL	N1901	14 Dec 65
214	18956	25	Eastern AL	N8142N	14 Dec 65
215	18993	21	Pan American	N315PA	29 Dec 65
216	18862	22	United AL	N7055U	29 Dec 65
217	18876	46	Japan AL	JA8309	30 Dec 65
218	19131	23	American AL	N1902	4 Jan 66
219	18994	21	Pan American	N316PA	6 Jan 66
220	18967	25	Eastern AL	N8143N	7 Jan 66
221	18995	21	Pan American	N317PA	11 Jan 66
222	18934	30	Lufthansa	D-ABIS	12 Jan 66
223	18968	25	Eastern AL	N8144N	18 Jan 66
224	18907	31	TWA	N842TW	22 Jan 66
225	18969	25	Eastern AL	N8145N	20 Jan 66
226	18877	46	Japan AL	JA8310	21 Jan 66
227	18863	22	United AL	N7056U	26 Jan 66
228	19132	23	American AL	N1903	31 Jan 66
229	18970	25	Eastern AL	N8146N	2 Feb 66
230	18971	25	Eastern AL	N8147N	4 Feb 66
231	18864	22	United AL	N7057U	9 Feb 66
232	18865	22	United AL	N7058U	10 Feb 66
233	18996	21	Pan American	N318PA	14 Feb 66
234	18935	30	Lufthansa	D-ABIT	18 Feb 66
235	18997	21	Pan American	N319PA	18 Feb 66
236	18878	46	Japan AL	JA8311	21 Feb 66
237	18951	81	All Nippon	JA8316	23 Feb 66
238	18990	14	Pacific SW AL	N975PS	25 Feb 66
239	18998	21	Pan American	N320PA	2 Mar 66
240	18999	21	Pan American	N321PA	8 Mar 66
241	18866	22	United AL	N7059U	4 Mar 66
242	18972	25	Eastern AL	N8148N	10 Mar 66
243	19127	59	Avianca	HK-727	16 Mar 66
244	18898	51C	NW Orient AL	N490US	29 Mar 66
245	18973	25	Eastern AL	N8149N	17 Mar 66
246	19138	89	Japan Dom AL	JA8314	18 Mar 66
247	18867	22	United AL	N7060U	22 Mar 66
248	18868	22	United AL	N7061U	25 Mar 66
249	18936	30	Lufthansa	D-ABIV	30 Mar 66
250	19089	22C	United AL	N7401U	7 Apr 66
251	19180	23	American AL	N1905	30 Mar 66
252	18947	25	Eastern AL	N8150N	6 Apr 66
253	18869	22	United AL	N7062U	5 Apr 66
254	18879	46	Japan AL	JA8312	7 Apr 66
255	19139	89	Japan Dom AL	JA8315	13 Apr 66
256	18899	51C	NW Orient AL	N491US	22 Apr 66
257	19005	21	Pan American	N323PA	17 Apr 66
258	18870	22	United AL	N7063U	19 Apr 66
259	18871	22	United AL	N7064U	18 Apr 66
260	19242	11	Wardair	CF-FUN	20 Apr 66
261	18872	22	United AL	N7065U	22 Apr 66
262	19006	21	Pan American	N324PA	27 Apr 66
263	18945	51C	NW Orient AL	N492US	2 May 66
264	19121	51	NW Orient AL	N475US	30 Apr 66
265	19181	23	American AL	N1906	3 May 66
266	19182	23	American AL	N1907	5 May 66
267	19183	23	American AL	N1908	6 May 66
268	19079	22	United AL	N7066U	18 May 66
269	19007	21	Pan American	N325PA	10 May 66
270	19080	22	United AL	N7067U	11 May 66
271	19109	27C	Braniff AW	N7270	22 May 66
272	19035	21	Pan American	N326PA	19 May 66
273	19243	162	Braniff AW	N7282	19 May 66
274	18946	51C	NW Orient AL	N493US	19 May 66
275	19081	22	United AL	N7068U	20 May 66
276	19171	86	Iran Air	EP-IRA	25 Jun 66

Line No	Constrn No	Model No	First Operator	Delivery Registration	First flight
277	19090	22C	United AL	N7402U	2 Jun 66
278	19036	21	Pan American	N327PA	27 May 66
279	19082	22	United AL	N7069U	27 May 66
280	19091	22C	United AL	N7403U	3 Jun 66
281	19083	22	United AL	N7070U	13 Jun 66
282	19184	23	American AL	N1909	10 Jun 66
283	19110	27C	Braniff AW	N7271	15 Jun 66
284	19037	21	Pan American	N328PA	15 Jun 66
285	19038	21	Pan American	N329PA	18 Jun 66
286	18947	51C	NW Orient AL	N494US	20 Jun 66
287	19304	193	Pacific AL	N2969G	24 Jun 66
288	19279	46	Japan AL	JA8318	24 Jun 66
289	19134	21C	Pan American	N339PA	29 Jun 66
290	19176	61	FAA	N127	1 Jul 66
291	19092	22C	United AL	N7404U	8 Jul 66
292	19165	35	National AL	N4620	12 Jul 66
293	19093	22C	United AL	N7405U	15 Jul 66
294	19206	51C	NW Orient AL	N495US	5 Aug 66
295	19094	22C	United AL	N7406U	18 Jul 66
296	19253	77	Ansett AL	VH-RMR	20 Jul 66
297	19111	27C	Braniff AW	N7272	21 Jul 66
298	19254	76	TAA	VH-TJD	24 Jul 66
299	19112	27C	Braniff AW	N7273	29 Jul 66
300	19305	193	Pacific AL	N2979G	28 Jul 66
301	19135	21C	Pan American	N340PA	1 Aug 66
302	19095	22C	United AL	N7407U	9 Aug 66
303	19166	35	National AL	N4621	12 Aug 66
304	19249	85	Northeast AL	N1633	16 Aug 66
305	19096	22C	United AL	N7408U	19 Aug 66
306	18952	81	All Nippon	JA8317	19 Aug 66
307	19097	22C	United AL	N7409U	23 Aug 66
308	19173	92C	Southern AT	N5055	9 Sep 66
309	19391	191	Frontier AL	N7270F	25 Aug 66
310	19113	27C	Braniff AW	N7274	26 Aug 66
311	19385	23	American AL	N1910	27 Aug 66
312	19114	27C	Braniff AW	N7275	1 Sep 66
313	19250	95	Northeast AL	N1634	1 Sep 66
314	19136	21C	Pan American	N341PA	29 Sep 66
315	19251	95	Northeast AL	N1635	10 Sep 66
316	19137	21C	Pan American	N342PA	9 Sep 66
317	19392	191	Frontier AL	N7271F	15 Sep 66
318	19098	22C	United AL	N7410U	18 Sep 66
319	19122	51	NW Orient AL	N476US	19 Sep 66
320	19169	90C	Alaska AL	N797AS	25 Sep 66
321	19386	23	American AL	N1928	25 Sep 66
322	19099	22C	United AL	N7411U	30 Sep 66
323	19172	86	Iran Air	EP-IRB	1 Oct 66
324	19100	22C	United AL	N7412U	6 Oct 66
325	19167	35	National AL	N4622	8 Oct 66
326	19174	92C	Southern AT	N5092	11 Oct 66
327	19252	95	Northeast AL	N1636	13 Oct 66
328	19115	27C	Braniff AW	N7276	16 Nov 66
329	19387	23	American AL	N1929	20 Oct 66
330	19116	27C	Braniff AW	N7277	22 Oct 66
331	19255	64	Mexicana	XA-SEJ	26 Oct 66
332	19170	90C	Alaska AL	N798AS	1 Nov 66
333	19101	22C	United AL	N7413U	4 Nov 66
334	19123	51	NW Orient AL	N477US	4 Nov 66
335	19298	25C	Eastern AL	N8151G	10 Nov 66
336	19102	22C	United AL	N7414U	14 Nov 66
337	19084	22	United AL	N7071U	8 Dec 66
338	19244	62C	Braniff AW	N7284	18 Nov 66
339	19175	92C	Air America	N5093	19 Nov 66
340	19388	23	American AL	N1930	16 Nov 66
341	19103	22C	United AL	N7415U	30 Nov 66
342	19245	62C	Braniff AW	N7286	30 Nov 66
343	19389	23	American AL	N1931	1 Dec 66
344	19299	25C	Eastern AL	N8152G	4 Dec 66
345	19398	14	PacificSW AL	N976PS	10 Dec 66
346	19300	25C	Eastern AL	N8153G	12 Dec 66
347	19124	51	NW Orient AL	N478US	9 Dec 66
348	19318	44	SAA	ZS-EKW	21 Dec 66
349	19085	22	United AL	N7072U	16 Dec 66
350	19390	23	American AL	N1932	19 Dec 66
351	19228	31	TWA	N889TW	18 Dec 66
352	19301	25C	Eastern AL	N8154G	3 Jan 67
353	19086	22	United AL	N7073U	14 Jan 67
354	19302	25C	Eastern AL	N8155G	12 Jan 67
355	19256	64	Mexicana	XA-SEL	6 Jan 67
356	19356	25C	Eastern AL	N8156G	10 Jan 67
357	19303	59	Avianca	HK-1337	3 Jan 67
358	19428	23	American AL	N1933	12 Jan 67
359	19087	22	United AL	N7074U	20 Jan 67
360	19357	25C	Eastern AL	N8157G	20 Jan 67
361	19125	51	NW Orient AL	N479US	17 Jan 67
362	19429	23	American AL	N1934	20 Jan 67
363	19126	51	NW Orient AL	N480US	21 Jan 67
364	19008	30C	Lufthansa	D-ABIW	9 Feb 67
365	19088	22	United AL	N7075U	26 Jan 67
366	19430	23	American AL	N1935	26 Jan 67
367	19358	25C	Eastern AL	N8158G	16 Feb 67
368	19359	25C	Eastern AL	N8159G	31 Jan 67
369	19140	22	United AL	N7076U	27 Jan 67
370	19141	22	United AL	N7077U	10 Feb 67
371	19360	25C	Eastern AL	N8160G	2 Feb 67
372	19431	23	American AL	N1955	3 Feb 67
373	19280	46	Japan AL	JA8319	10 Feb 67
374	19009	30C	Lufthansa	D-ABIX	20 Feb 67
375	19427	64	Mexicana	XA-SEM	7 Feb 67
376	19117	27C	Braniff AW	N7278	16 Feb 67
377	19620	193	Pacific AL	N898PC	17 Feb 67
378	19281	46	Japan AL	JA8320	17 Feb 67
379	19118	27C	Braniff AW	N7279	21 Feb 67
380	19399	109	China AL	B-1818	24 Feb 67
381	19432	23	American AL	N1956	27 Feb 67
382	19010	30C	Lufthansa	D-ABIZ	28 Feb 67
383	19287	51C	NW Orient AL	N496US	1 Mar 67
384	19404	82	TAP	CS-TBK	6 Mar 67
385	19257	21	Pan American	N355PA	4 Mar 67
386	19191	22C	United AL	N7416U	9 Mar 67
387	19011	30C	Lufthansa	D-ABIA	23 Mar 67
388	19192	22C	United AL	N7417U	10 Mar 67
389	19288	51C	NW Orient AL	N497US	13 Mar 67
390	19229	31C	TWA	N890TW	23 Mar 67
391	19012	30C	Lufthansa	D-ABIE	6 Apr 67
392	19193	22C	United AL	N7418U	23 Mar 67
393	19119	27C	Braniff AW	N7280	29 Mar 67
394	19194	22C	United AL	N7419U	3 Apr 67
395	19310	30C	Lufthansa	D-ABII	6 Apr 67
396	19120	27C	Braniff AW	N7281	6 Apr 67
397	19258	21	Pan American	N356PA	6 Apr 67
398	19405	82	TAP	CS-TBL	10 Apr 67
399	19311	30C	Lufthansa	D-ABID	13 Apr 67
400	19400	29	Sabena	OO-STA	16 Apr 67
401	19393	191	Frontier AL	N7272F	14 Apr 67
402	19230	31C	TWA	N891TW	19 Apr 67
403	19289	51C	NW Orient AL	N498US	16 Apr 67
404	19231	31C	TWA	N892TW	25 Apr 67
405	19557	81	All Nippon	JA 8321	25 Apr 67
406	19195	22C	United AL	N7420U	28 Apr 67
407	19196	22C	United AL	N7421U	3 May 67
408	19259	21	Pan American	N357PA	2 May 67
409	19312	30C	Lufthansa	D-ABIU	5 May 67
410	19197	22C	United AL	N7422U	9 May 67
411	19313	30C	Lufthansa	D-ABIY	11 May 67
412	19260	21	Pan American	N358PA	12 May 67
413	19198	22C	United AL	N7423U	17 May 67
414	19199	22C	United AL	N7424U	19 May 67
415	19402	29C	Sabena	OO-STB	25 Jul 67
416	19200	22C	United AL	N7425U	25 May 67
417	19290	51C	NW Orient AL	N499US	20 May 67
418	19394	191	Frontier AL	N7273F	26 May 67
419	19401	29	Sabena	OO-STC	1 Jun 67
420	19503	108C	Icelandair	TF-FIE	6 Jun 67

Line No	Constrn No	Model No	First Operator	Delivery Registration	First flight
421	19201	22C	United AL	N7426U	13 Jun 67
422	19261	21	Pan American	N359PA	7 Jun 67
423	19246	62C	Braniff AW	N7287	5 Jun 67
424	19202	22C	United AL	N7427U	16 Jun 67
425	19232	31C	TWA	N893TW	16 Jun 67
426	19262	21	Pan American	N360PA	16 Jun 67
427	19504	173C	World AW	N690WA	26 Jun 67
428	19524	24C	Continental AW	N2471	23 Jun 67
429	19497	27C	Braniff AW	N7288	23 Jun 67
430	19406	82	TAP	CS-TBM	28 Jun 67
431	19395	191	Frontier AL	N7274F	29 Jun 67
432	19505	173C	World AW	N691WA	5 Jul 67
433	19536	200	Boeing	N7270L	27 Jul 67
434	19203	22C	United AL	N7428U	7 Jul 67
435	19403	29C	Sabena	OO-STD	11 Jul 67
436	19204	22C	United AL	N7429U	11 Jul 67
437	19314	30C	Lufthansa	D-ABIJ	14 Jul 67
438	19205	22C	United AL	N7430U	18 Jul 67
439	19525	24C	Continental AL	N2472	20 Jul 67
440	19142	22	United AL	N7078U	24 Jul 67
441	19319	44	SAA	ZS-EKX	24 Jul 67
442	19526	24C	Continental AL	N2473	25 Jul 67
443	19815	114	PacificSW AL	N977PS	28 Jul 67
444	19499	27	Braniff AW	N7289	29 Jul 67
445	19444	295	Northeast AL	N1639	16 Aug 67
446	19143	22	United AL	N7079U	4 Aug 67
447	19506	173C	World AW	N692WA	4 Aug 67
448	19500	27	Braniff AW	N7290	4 Aug 67
449	19507	173C	World AW	N693WA	25 Aug 67
450	19144	22	United AL	N7080U	11 Aug 67
451	19145	22	United AL	N7081U	11 Aug 67
452	19146	22	United AL	N7082U	17 Aug 67
453	19501	27	Braniff AW	N7292	23 Aug 67
454	19534	27	Braniff AW	N7293	29 Aug 67
455	19445	295	Northeast AL	N1640	1 Sep 67
456	19535	27	Braniff AW	N7294	25 Aug 67
457	19508	173C	World AW	N694WA	30 Aug 67
458	19233	31C	TWA	N894TW	1 Sep 67
459	19509	173C	World AW	N695WA	6 Sep 67
460	19527	24C	Continental AL	N2474	7 Sep 67
461	19618	155C	Exec Jet Av	N530EJ	8 Sep 67
462	19818	121C	Pan American	N388PA	9 Sep 67
463	19234	31C	TWA	N895TW	14 Sep 67
464	19450	235	National AL	N4730	17 Nov 67
465	19528	24C	Continental AL	N2475	16 Sep 67
466	19520	109	China AL	B-1820	16 Sep 67
467	19595	95	Northeast AL	N1637	14 Sep 67
468	19717	25C	Eastern AL	M8161G	19 Sep 67
469	19532	27C	Braniff AW	N7295	22 Sep 67
470	19619	155C	Exec Jet Av	N531EJ	26 Sep 67
471	19446	295	Northeast AL	N1641	20 Nov 67
472	19147	22	United AL	N7083U	2 Oct 67
473	19148	22	United AL	N7084U	2 Oct 67
474	19718	25C	Eastern AL	N8162G	4 Oct 67
475	19533	27C	Braniff AW	N7296	6 Oct 67
476	19665	172C	Airlift Int	N725AL	6 Oct 67
477	19447	295	Northeast AL	N1642	29 Nov 67
478	19719	25C	Eastern AL	N8163G	11 Oct 67
479	19596	95	Northeast AL	N1638	11 Oct 67
480	19666	172C	Airlift Int	N726AL	17 Oct 67
481	19149	22	United AL	N7085U	18 Oct 67
482	19720	25C	Eastern AL	N8164G	19 Oct 67
483	19451	235	National AL	N4731	4 Dec 67
484	19662	59	Avianca	HK-1400	20 Oct 67
485	19150	22	United AL	N7086	25 Oct 67
486	19833	35	American AL	N1957	26 Oct 67
487	19691	134	Transair	SE-DDA	2 Nov 67
488	19683	214	Pacific SW AL	N528PS	7 Dec 67
489	19834	35	American AL	N1958	1 Nov 67
490	19721	25C	Eastern AL	N8165G	3 Nov 67
491	19663	59	Avianca	HK-1401	6 Nov 67
492	19452	235	National AL	N4732	14 Dec 67
493	19722	25C	Eastern AL	N8166G	9 Nov 67
494	19836	95	American AL	N1962	13 Nov 67
495	19282	46	Japan AL	JA8325	13 Nov 67
496	19448	295	Northeast AL	N1643	19 Dec 67
497	19850	25C	Eastern AL	N8167G	12 Nov 67
498	19692	134	Transair	SE-DDB	20 Nov 67
499	19837	95	American AL	N1963	22 Nov 67
500	19449	295	Northeast AL	N1644	28 Dec 67
501	19835	35	American AL	N1959	29 Nov 67
502	19283	46	Japan AL	JA8326	30 Nov 67
503	19684	214	Pacific SW AL	N583PS	3 Jan 68
504	19151	22	United AL	N7087U	3 Dec 67
505	19816	86	Iran Air	EP-IRC	7 Dec 67
506	19453	235	National AL	N4733	5 Jan 68
507	19152	22	United AL	N7088U	11 Dec 67
508	19153	22	United AL	N7089U	12 Dec 67
509	19454	235	National AL	N4734	9 Jan 68
510	19851	25C	Eastern AL	N8168G	19 Dec 67
511	19475	223	American AL	N6800	20 Jan 68
512	19154	22	United AL	N7090U	18 Dec 67
513	19455	235	National AL	N4735	12 Jan 68
514	19867	151C	NW Orient AL	N488US	29 Dec 67
515	19456	235	National AL	N4736	13 Jan 68
516	19819	121C	Pan American	N389PA	4 Jan 68
517	19852	25C	Eastern AL	N8169G	10 Jan 68
518	19457	235	National AL	N4737	24 Jan 68
519	19793	30C	Lufthansa	D-ABBI	10 Jan 68
520	19811	116	LAN-Chile	CC-CAG	12 Jan 68
521	19991	291	Frontier AL	N7276F	27 Jan 68
522	19853	25C	Eastern AL	N8170G	20 Jan 68
523	19476	223	American AL	N6801	3 Feb 68
524	19597	82C	TAP	CS-TBN	24 Jan 68
525	19458	235	National AL	N4738	2 Feb 68
526	19992	291	Frontier AL	N7277F	9 Feb 68
527	19827	185C	Amer'n Flyers	N12827	26 Jan 68
528	19558	231	TWA	N12301	16 Feb 68
529	19868	151C	NW Orient AL	N489US	29 Jan 68
530	19459	235	National AL	N4739	14 Feb 68
531	19460	235	National AL	N4740	16 Feb 68
532	19812	116	LAN-Chile	CC-CAQ	2 Feb 68
533	19477	223	American AL	N6802	16 Feb 68
534	19874	180C	TWA	N9515T	7 Feb 68
535	19478	223	American AL	N6803	21 Feb 68
536	19728	90C	Alaska AL	N766AS	17 Feb 68
537	19817	86	Iran Air	EP-IRD	17 Feb 68
538	19461	235	National AL	N4741	27 Feb 68
539	19462	235	National AL	N4742	29 Feb 68
540	19690	113C	Ariana Afghan	YA-FAR	22 Feb 68
541	19543	228	Air France	F-BOJA	9 Mar 68
542	19839	123	American AL	N1965	23 Feb 68
543	19805	22C	United AL	N7431U	1 Mar 68
544	19479	223	American AL	N6804	8 Mar 68
545	19480	223	American AL	N6805	12 Mar 68
546	19826	185C	Amer'n Flyers	N12826	5 Mar 68
547	19806	22C	United AL	N7432U	14 Mar 68
548	19481	223	American AL	N6806	13 Mar 68
549	19993	291	Frontier AL	N7278F	13 Mar 68
550	19559	231	TWA	N12302	16 Mar 68
551	19838	123	American AL	N1964	18 Mar 68
552	19463	235	National AL	N4743	20 Mar 68
553	19464	235	National AL	N4744	20 Mar 68
554	19465	235	National AL	N4745	22 Mar 68
555	19846	63	Faucett	OB-R-902	26 Mar 68
556	19685	214	Pacific SW AL	N530PS	27 Mar 68
557	19482	223	American AL	N6807	2 Apr 68
558	19483	223	American AL	N6808	4 Apr 68
559	19859	171C	Trans Int AL	N1727T	3 Apr 68
560	19484	223	American AL	N6809	8 Apr 68
561	19466	235	National AL	N4746	5 Apr 68
562	19544	228	Air France	F-BOJB	10 Apr 68
563	19537	222	United AL	N7620U	18 Apr 68
564	19545	228	Air France	F-BOJC	19 Apr 68

Line No	Constrn No	Model No	First Operator	Delivery Registration	First flight
565	19560	231	TWA	N12303	19 Apr 68
566	19467	235	National AL	N4747	19 Apr 68
567	19468	235	National AL	N4748	20 Apr 68
568	19469	235	National AL	N4749	24 Apr 68
569	19470	235	National AL	N4750	24 Apr 68
570	19686	214	Pacific SW AL	N531PS	25 Apr 68
571	19485	223	American AL	N6810	1 May 68
572	19546	228	Air France	F-BOJD	3 May 68
573	19687	214	Pacific SW AL	N532PS	2 May 68
574	19561	231	TWA	N12304	6 May 68
575	19807	172C	Airlift Int	N727AL	7 May 68
576	19562	231	TWA	N12305	10 May 68
577	19510	224	Continental AL	N88701	11 May 68
578	19486	223	American AL	N6811	14 May 68
579	19487	223	American AL	N6812	14 May 68
580	19538	222	United AL	N7631U	17 May 68
581	19511	224	Continental AL	N88701	17 May 68
582	19512	224	Continental AL	N88702	20 May 68
583	19539	222	United AL	N7622U	22 May 68
584	19540	222	United AL	N7623U	31 May 68
585	19541	222	United AL	N7624U	8 Jun 68
586	19542	222	United AL	N7625U	8 Jun 68
587	19563	231	TWA	N12306	3 Jun 68
588	19488	223	American AL	N6813	4 Jun 68
589	19688	214	Pacific SW AL	N533PS	4 Jun 68
590	19471	235	National AL	N4751	6 Jun 68
591	19472	235	National AL	N4752	11 Jun 68
592	20044	23	American AL	N1969	13 Jun 68
593	19489	223	American AL	N6814	14 Jun 68
594	19813	116C	LAN-Chile	CC-CFD	13 Jun 68
595	19513	224	Continental AL	N88703	18 Jun 68
596	20045	23	American AL	N2913	25 Jun 68
597	19514	224	Continental AL	N88704	21 Jun 68
598	19797	224	Continental AL	N88706	20 Jun 68
599	19860	171C	Trans Int	N1728T	27 Jun 68
600	19814	116C	LAN-Chile	CC-CFE	25 Jun 68
601	19564	231	TWA	N12307	28 Jun 68
602	19490	223	American AL	N6815	2 Jul 68
603	19575	231	TWA	N12308	9 Jul 68
604	19873	180C	TWA	N9516T	8 Jun 68
605	20046	23	American AL	N2914	10 Jul 68
606	19473	235	National AL	N4753	9 Jul 68
607	19474	235	National AL	N4754	12 Jul 68
608	19798	224	Continental AL	N88707	16 Jul 68
609	19828	231	TWA	N52309	17 Jul 68
610	19689	214	Pacific SW AL	N534PS	16 Jul 68
611	19491	223	American AL	N6816	19 Jul 68
612	19799	224	Continental AL	N88708	23 Jul 68
613	20139	295	Northeast AL	N1645	30 Sep 68
614	19899	222	United AL	N7626U	26 Jul 68
615	19808	172C	Airlift Int	N732AL	29 Jul 68
616	19800	224	Continental AL	N88709	31 Jul 68
617	19801	224	Continental AL	N88710	1 Aug 68
618	19900	222	United AL	N7627U	6 Aug 68
619	20143	1A7C	Trans Carib	N8789R	6 Aug 68
620	19901	222	United AL	N7628U	9 Aug 68
621	19802	224	Continental AL	N88711	7 Aug 68
622	19902	222	United AL	N7629U	22 Aug 68
623	19803	224	Continental AL	N88712	13 Aug 58
624	19804	224	Continental AL	N88713	15 Aug 68
625	20217	116	Braniff	N304BN	20 Aug 68
626	20042	134C	Transair	SE-DDC	22 Aug 68
627	19903	222	United AL	N7630U	28 Aug 68
628	19854	25C	Eastern AL	N8171G	27 Aug 68
629	19829	231	TWA	N52310	29 Aug 68
630	19890	22C	United AL	N7433U	30 Aug 68
631	19891	22C	United AL	N7434U	4 Sep 68
632	19855	25C	Eastern AL	N8172G	4 Sep 68
633	19830	231	TWA	N52311	6 Sep 68
634	19987	29C	Sabena	OO-STE	11 Sep 68
635	19856	25C	Eastern AL	N8173G	12 Sep 68
636	19831	231	TWA	N52312	13 Sep 68
637	19904	222	United AL	N7631U	24 Sep 68
638	20140	295	Northeast AL	N1646	14 Oct 68
639	19905	222	United AL	N7632U	30 Sep 68
640	19892	22C	United AL	N7435U	24 Sep 68
641	19857	25C	Eastern AL	N8174G	24 Sep 68
642	19832	231	TWA	N52313	27 Sep 68
643	19893	22C	United AL	N7436U	28 Sep 68
644	19906	222	United AL	N7633U	10 Oct 68
645	19858	25C	Eastern AL	N8175G	1 Oct 68
646	20243	224	Continental AL	N88714	11 Oct 68
647	19894	22C	United AL	N7437U	26 Oct 68
648	19970	251	NW Orient AL	N251US	11 Oct 68
649	20141	295	Northeast AL	N1647	5 Nov 68
650	20244	224	Libyan Arab AL	5A-DAH	16 Oct 68
651	19907	222	United AL	N7634U	30 Oct 68
652	19492	223	American AL	N6817	23 Oct 68
653	19908	222	United AL	N7635U	11 Nov 68
654	19994	291	Northeast AL	N1648	1 Oct 68
655	19971	251	NW Orient AL	N252US	26 Oct 68
656	19909	222	United AL	N7636U	11 Nov 68
657	19493	223	American AL	N6818	6 Nov 68
658	19895	22C	United AL	N7438U	6 Nov 68
659	19910	222	United AL	N7637U	4 Dec 68
660	19968	82C	TAP	CS-TBO	12 Nov 68
661	19494	223	American AL	N6819	12 Nov 68
662	19972	251	NW Orient AL	N253US	15 Nov 68
663	20245	224	Libyan Arab AL	5A-DAI	13 Jan 69
664	19495	223	American AL	N6820	19 Nov 68
665	19973	251	NW Orient AL	N254US	19 Nov 68
666	19995	291	Northeast AL	N1649	13 Jan 69
667	19974	251	NW Orient AL	N255US	27 Nov 68
668	1911	222	United AL	N7638U	12 Dec 68
669	19496	223	American AL	N6821	4 Dec 68
670	19912	222	United AL	N7639U	18 Dec 68
671	20003	284	Olympic AW	SX-CBA	11 Dec 68
672	19913	222	United AL	N7640U	19 Dec 68
673	19700	223	American AL	N6822	14 Dec 68
674	19975	251	NW Orient AL	N256US	18 Dec 68
675	20047	231	TWA	N94314	30 Dec 68
676	19914	222	United AL	N7641U	3 Jan 69
677	19701	223	American AL	N6823	6 Jan 69
678	20004	284	Olympic AW	SX-CBB	4 Jan 69
679	20048	231	TWA	N64315	9 Jan 69
680	19702	223	American AL	N6824	8 Jan 69
681	19915	222	United AL	N7642U	17 Jan 69
682	19861	228	Air France	F-BOJE	15 Jan 69
683	19976	251	NW Orient AL	N257US	16 Jan 69
684	19703	223	American AL	N6825	21 Jan 69
685	19862	228	Air France	F-BOJF	23 Jan 69
686	20078	46	Japan AL	JA8327	22 Jan 69
687	20005	284	Olympic AW	SX-CBC	29 Jan 69
688	20006	284	Olympic AW	SX-CBD	30 Jan 69
689	19704	223	American AL	N6826	30 Jan 69
690	19977	251	NW Orient AL	N258US	5 Feb 69
691	19863	228	Air France	F-BPJG	6 Feb 69
692	19978	251	NW Orient AL	N259US	11 Feb 69
693	20049	231	TWA	N44316	13 Feb 69
694	20050	231	TWA	N74317	20 Feb 69
695	20111	109C	China AL	B-1822	19 Feb 69
696	19864	228	Air France	F-BPJH	19 Feb 69
697	19979	251	NW Orient AL	N260US	21 Feb 69
698	20180	223	American AL	N6827	27 Feb 69
699	20181	223	American AL	N6828	28 Feb 69
700	20112	31	TWA	N7890	14 Apr 69
701	20037	222	United AL	N7643U	7 Mar 69
702	20182	223	American AL	N6829	11 Mar 69
703	19865	228	Air France	F-BPJI	13 Mar 69
704	20075	228	Air France	F-BPJJ	14 Mar 69
705	20183	223	American AL	N6830	21 Mar 69
706	19980	251	NW Orient AL	N261US	20 Mar 69

Line No	Constrn No	Model No	First Operator	Delivery Registration	First flight
707	20184	223	American AL	N6831	24 Mar 69
708	20051	231	TWA	N74318	1 Apr 69
709	20052	231	TWA	N64319	3 Apr 69
710	20185	223	American AL	N6832	2 Apr 69
711	20113	31	TWA	N97891	16 Apr 69
712	20114	31	TWA	N7892	9 Apr 69
713	20053	231	TWA	N64320	21 Apr 69
714	20161	214	Pacific SW AL	N535PS	14 Apr 69
715	20162	214	Frontier AL	N7279F	18 Apr 69
716	20038	222	United AL	N7644U	24 Apr 69
717	20240	2A7	Trans Carib	N8790R	24 Apr 69
718	20054	231	TWA	N64321	29 Apr 69
719	20055	231	TWA	N64322	6 May 69
720	20039	222	United AL	N7645U	13 May 69
721	20186	223	American AL	N6833	13 May 69
722	20187	223	American AL	N6834	15 May 69
723	20163	214	Pacific SW AL	N537PS	14 May 69
724	20164	214	Pacific SW AL	N538PS	20 May 69
725	20165	214	Pacific SW AL	N539PS	21 May 69
726	20241	2A7	Trans Carib	N8791R	20 May 69
727	20166	214	Pacific SW AL	N540PS	28 May 69
728	20167	214	Pacific SW AL	N541PS	2 Jun 69
729	20040	222	United AL	N7646U	8 Jun 69
730	20188	223	American AL	N6835	11 Jun 69
731	20098	231	TWA	N64323	12 Jun 69
732	20041	222	United AL	N7647U	18 Jun 69
733	20189	223	American AL	N6836	19 Jun 69
734	20099	231	TWA	N64324	20 Jun 69
735	20115	31	TWA	N7893	25 Jun 69
736	19981	251	NW Orient AL	N262US	30 Jun 69
737	19982	251	NW Orient AL	N263US	7 Jul 69
738	20190	223	American AL	N6837	9 Jul 69
739	20191	223	American AL	N6838	14 Jul 69
740	20168	214	Pacific SW AL	N542PS	4 Jul 69
741	19983	251	NW Orient AL	N264US	18 Jul 69
742	20144	225	Eastern AL	N8825E	22 Jul 69
743	20169	214	Pacific SW AL	N543PS	22 Jul 69
744	19984	251	NW Orient AL	N265US	28 Jul 69
745	19985	251	NW Orient AL	N266US	4 Aug 69
746	20289	251	NW Orient AL	N267US	5 Aug 69
747	20290	251	NW Orient AL	N268US	7 Aug 69
748	20278	1A0	Lloyd Aero	CP-861	12 Aug 69
749	20145	225	Eastern AL	N8826E	18 Aug 69
750	20263	247	Western AL	N2801W	21 Aug 69
751	20146	225	Eastern AL	N8827E	29 Aug 69
752	20192	223	American AL	N6839	27 Aug 69
753	20291	251	NW Orient AL	N269US	3 Sep 69
754	20292	251	NW Orient AL	N270US	5 Sep 69
755	20193	223	American AL	N6841	11 Sep 69
756	20264	247	Western AL	N2802W	11 Sep 69
757	20293	251	NW Orient AL	N271US	12 Sep 69
758	20265	247	Western AL	N2803W	23 Sep 69
759	20294	251	NW Orient AL	N272US	18 Sep 69
760	20266	247	Western AL	N2804W	24 Oct 69
761	20248	295	Northeast AL	N1650	30 Sep 69
762	20267	247	Western AL	N2805W	29 Oct 69
763	20249	295	Northeast AL	N1651	7 Oct 69
764	20268	247	Western AL	N2806W	30 Oct 69
765	20201	284	Olympic AW	SX-CBE	15 Oct 69
766	20228	76	TAA	VH-TJE	16 Oct 69
767	20147	225	Eastern AL	N8828E	23 Oct 69
768	20278	77C	Ansett AL	VH-RMS	20 Oct 69
769	20148	225	Eastern AL	N8829E	30 Oct 69
770	20149	225	Eastern AL	N8830E	3 Nov 69
771	20150	225	Eastern AL	N8831E	5 Nov 69
772	20295	251	NW Orient AL	N273US	6 Nov 69
773	20151	225	Eastern AL	N8832E	17 Nov 69
774	20202	228	Air France	F-BPJK	17 Nov 69
775	20152	225	Eastern AL	N8833E	17 Nov 69
776	20203	228	Air France	F-BPJL	21 Nov 69
777	20296	251	NW Orient AL	N274US	1 Dec 69
778	20204	228	Air France	F-BPJM	1 Dec 69
779	20153	225	Eastern AL	N8834E	2 Dec 69
780	20154	225	Eastern AL	N8835E	5 Dec 69
781	20250	254	Pacific SW AL	N547PS	10 Dec 69
782	20251	254	Pacific SW AL	N548PS	15 Dec 69
783	20252	254	Pacific SW AL	N549PS	23 Dec 69
784	20343	113C	Ariana Afghan	YA-FAU	30 Dec 69
785	20232	231	TWA	N54325	8 Jan 70
786	20233	231	TWA	N54326	15 Jan 70
787	20435	281	All Nippon	JA8328	15 Feb 70
788	20436	281	All Nippon	JA8329	2 Mar 71
789	20302	2B7	Allegheny AL	N750VJ	27 Jan 70
790	20234	231	TWA	N54327	4 Feb 70
791	20306	231	TWA	N54328	13 Feb 70
792	20307	231	TWA	N54329	24 Feb 70
793	20303	2B7	Allegheny AL	N751VJ	16 Apr 70
794	20384	224	Continental AL	N88715	1 Feb 70
795	20308	231	TWA	N54330	19 Mar 70
796	20309	231	TWA	N54331	20 Mar 70
797	20327	17	CP Air	CF-CPN	26 Feb 70
798	20437	254	Pacific SW AL	N384PS	2 Mar 70
799	20438	254	Pacific SW AL	N536PS	25 Mar 70
800	20385	224	Continental AL	N32716	10 Mar 70
801	20386	224	Continental AL	N32717	16 Mar 70
802	20310	231	TWA	N54332	30 Mar 70
803	20422	41	Varig	PP-VLF	23 Sep 70
804	20387	224	Continental AL	N32718	31 Mar 70
805	20388	224	Continental AL	N32719	3 Apr 70
806	20328	17	CP Air	CF-CPK	8 Apr 70
807	20463	224	Continental AL	N32721	16 Oct 70
808	20304	2B6	RAM	CN-CCF	21 Apr 70
809	20464	224	Continental AL	N32722	22 Oct 70
810	20423	41	Varig	PP-VLG	25 Sep 70
811	20392	227	Braniff AW	N401BN	4 May 70
812	20418	C3	Cruzeiro	PP-CJE	20 Oct 70
813	20393	227	Braniff AW	N402BN	12 May 70
814	20465	224	Continental AL	N32723	28 Oct 70
815	20419	C3	Cruzeiro	PP-CJF	27 Oct 70
816	20394	227	Braniff AW	N403BN	17 Jun 70
817	20424	41	Varig	PP-VLH	5 Oct 70
818	20379	225	Eastern AL	N8836E	8 Jun 70
819	20420	C3	Cruzeiro	PP-CJG	2 Nov 70
820	20380	225	Eastern AL	N8837E	19 Jun 70
821	20370	77C	Ansett AL	VH-RMT	24 Jun 70
822	20371	76	TAA	VH-TJF	30 Jun 70
823	20381	225	Eastern AL	N8838E	2 Jul 70
824	20425	41	Varig	PP-VLD	14 Oct 70
825	20382	225	Eastern AL	N8839E	13 Jul 70
826	20421	1F8	Royal Nepal	9N-ABD	19 Mar 71
827	20432	26A	Mexicana	XA-TAA	24 Jul 70
828	20366	214	Pacific AL	N546PS	9 Nov 70
829	20426	1J1	Dominicana	HI-212	19 Mar 71
830	20430	230	Lufthansa	D-ABEL	11 Sep 71
831	20383	225	Eastern AL	N8840E	11 Aug 70
832	20367	214	Pacific AL	N544PS	25 Sep 70
833	20415	225	Eastern AL	N8841E	24 Aug 70
834	20416	225	Eastern AL	N8842E	25 Aug 70
835	20441	225	Eastern AL	N8843E	28 Aug 70
836	20442	225	Eastern AL	N8844E	4 Sep 70
837	20443	225	Eastern AL	N8845E	23 Oct 70
838	20433	264	Mexicana	XA-TAB	12 Oct 70
839	20444	225	Eastern AL	N8846E	27 Oct 70
840	20445	225	Eastern AL	N8847E	29 Oct 70
841	20446	225	Eastern AL	N8848E	2 Nov 70
842	20434	264	Mexicana	XA-TAC	23 Oct 70
843	20447	225	Eastern AL	N8849E	4 Nov 70
844	20448	225	Eastern AL	N8850E	11 Nov 70
845	20409	228	Air France	F-BPJN	17 Nov 70
846	20410	228	Air France	F-BPJO	25 Nov 70
847	20411	228	Air France	F-BPJP	3 Dec 70
848	20471	2B6	RAM	CN-CCG	24 Nov 70
849	20468	281	All Nippon	JA8330	29 Dec 70
850	20472	2D6	Air Algerie	7T-VEA	14 Jan 71

Line No	Constrn No	Model No	First Operator	Delivery Registration	First flight
851	20431	230	Lufthansa	D-ABDI	26 Feb 71
852	20469	281	All Nippon	JA8331	29 Dec 70
853	20470	228	Air France	F-BPJQ	17 Feb 71
854	20474	44C	SAA	ZS-SBH	26 Jan 71
855	20473	2D6	Air Algerie	7T-VEB	3 Mar 71
856	20489	82	TAP	CS-TBP	22 Jan 71
857	20476	44C	SAA	ZS-SBI	18 Feb 71
858	20512	17	CP Air	CF-CUR	26 Feb 71
859	20460	231	TWA	N54333	19 Mar 71
860	20641	231	TWA	N54334	25 Mar 71
861	20513	17	CP Air	CF-CUS	8 Apr 71
862	20462	231	TWA	N54335	23 Apr 71
863	20490	231	TWA	N54336	3 May 71
864	20491	231	TWA	N54337	18 May 71
865	20466	281	All Nippon	JA8332	7 Jun 71
866	20467	281	All Nippon	JA8333	18 Jun 71
867	20509	281	All Nippon	JA8334	7 Aug 71
868	20285	281	All Nippon	JA8335	6 Aug 71
869	20533	1H2	ITT Corp	N320HG	23 Aug 71
870	20525	230	Lufthansa	D-ABFI	3 Sep 71
871	20526	230	Lufthansa	D-ABGI	19 Oct 71
872	20528	228	Air France	F-BPJR	7 Oct 71
873	20539	228	Air France	F-BPJS	22 Oct 71
874	20540	228	Air France	F-BPJT	5 Nov 71
875	20286	281	All Nippon	JA8336	1 Dec 71
876	20510	281	All Nippon	JA8337	17 Dec 71
877	20545	2H3	Tunis Air	TS-JHN	29 Jan 72
878	20568	281	All Nippon	JA8338	28 Jan 72
879	20569	281	All Nippon	JA8339	15 Mar 72
880	20570	281	All Nippon	JA8340	1 Mar 72
881	20752	281	All Nippon	JA8343	29 Feb 72
882	20592	256	Iberia	EC-CAI	13 Mar 72
883	20593	256	Iberia	EC-CAJ	31 Mar 72
884	20571	281	All Nippon	JA8341	17 Apr 72
885	20594	256	Iberia	EC-CAK	26 Apr 72
886	20579	247	Western AL	N2807W	14 May 72
887	20560	230	Lufthansa	D-ABHI	12 Mar 72
888	20573	281	All Nippon	JA8344	15 Apr 72
889	20580	247	Western AL	N2808W	6 Jun 72
890	20581	247	Western AL	N2809W	9 Jun 72
891	20608	227	Braniff AW	N410BN	20 Jun 72
892	20609	227	Braniff AW	N411BN	29 Jun 72
893	20610	227	Braniff AW	N412BN	10 Jul 72
894	20611	227	Braniff AW	N413BN	20 Jul 72
895	20648	247	Western AL	N2810W	26 Jul 72
896	20649	247	Western AL	N2811W	7 Aug 72
897	20614	225	Eastern AL	N8851E	14 Sep 72
898	20615	225	Eastern AL	N8852E	19 Sep 72
899	20616	225	Eastern AL	N8853E	27 Sep 72
900	20617	225	Eastern AL	N8855E	4 Oct 72
901	20618	225	Eastern AL	N8856E	5 Oct 72
902	20619	225	Eastern AL	N8857E	10 Oct 72
903	20620	225	Eastern AL	N8858E	13 Oct 72
904	20621	225	Eastern AL	N8859E	17 Oct 72
905	20595	256	Iberia	EC-CBA	23 Oct 72
906	20552	276	TAA	VH-TBG	2 Nov 72
907	20548	277	Ansett AL	VH-RMU	10 Nov 72
908	20596	256	Iberia	EC-CBB	30 Nov 72
909	20597	256	Iberia	EC-CBC	16 Nov 72
910	20598	256	Iberia	EC-CBD	21 Nov 72
911	20599	256	Iberia	EC-CBE	29 Nov 72
912	20600	256	Iberia	EC-CBF	5 Dec 72
913	20601	256	Iberia	EC-CBG	14 Dec 72
914	20602	256	Iberia	EC-CBH	19 Dec 72
915	20603	256	Iberia	EC-CBI	21 Dec 72
916	20604	256	Iberia	EC-CBJ	5 Jan 73
917	20634	232	Delta AL	N452DA	15 Jan 73
918	20635	232	Delta AL	N453DA	17 Jan 73
919	20636	232	Delta AL	N454DA	22 Jan 73
920	20637	232	Delta AL	N455DA	26 Jan 73
921	20605	256	Iberia	EC-CBK	2 Feb 73
922	20673	230	Lufthansa	D-ABKI	5 Feb 73
923	20674	230	Lufthansa	D-ABLI	13 Feb 73
924	20675	230	Condor	D-ABMI	19 Feb 73
925	20676	230	Condor	D-ABNI	22 Feb 73
926	20635	232	Delta AL	N456DA	14 Mar 73
927	20639	232	Delta AL	N457DA	16 Mar 73
928	20612	227	Braniff AW	N414BN	5 Mar 73
929	20613	227	Braniff AW	N415BN	7 Mar 73
930	20654	224	Continental	N32724	19 Mar 73
931	20678	214	Pacific AL	N550PS	21 Mar 73
932	20677	230	Condor	D-ABPI	22 Mar 73
933	20622	225	Eastern AL	N8860E	27 Mar 73
934	20655	224	Continental	N32725	30 Mar 73
935	20640	232	Delta AL	N458DA	20 Apr 73
936	20641	232	Delta AL	N459DA	24 Apr 73
937	20606	256	Iberia	EC-CBL	12 Apr 73
938	20656	224	Continental AL	N66726	18 Apr 73
939	20623	225	Eastern AL	N8861E	20 Apr 73
940	20624	225	Eastern AL	N8862E	25 Apr 73
941	20625	225	Eastern AL	N8863E	30 Apr 73
942	20679	214	Pacific SW AL	N551PS	3 May 73
943	20607	256	Iberia	EC-CBM	8 May 73
944	20642	232	Delta AL	N460DA	18 May 73
945	20705	2B6	RAM	CN-CCH	7 May 73
946	20626	225	Eastern AL	N8864E	21 May 73
947	20627	225	Eastern AL	N8865E	24 May 73
948	20628	225	Eastern AL	N8866E	30 May 73
949	20706	2J7	Pacific SW AL	N552PS	4 Jun 73
950	20709	264	Mexicana	XA-CUB	6 Jun 73
951	20643	232	Delta AL	N461DA	14 Jun 73
952	20739	2H3	Tunis Air	TS-JHO	14 Jun 73
953	20707	2J7	Pacific SW AL	N553PS	13 Jun 73
954	20724	281	All Nippon	JA8345	25 Jun 73
955	20729	227	Braniff AW	N416BN	28 Jun 73
956	20730	227	Braniff AW	N417BN	3 Jul 73
957	20731	227	Braniff AW	N418BN	9 Jul 73
958	20725	281	All Nippon	JA8346	7 Jul 73
959	20644	232	Delta AL	N462DA	18 Jul 73
960	20764	2J4	Sterling AW	OY-SAU	26 Jul 73
961	20645	232	Delta AL	N463DA	23 Jul 73
962	20726	281	All Nippon	JA8347	31 Jul 73
963	20732	227	Braniff AW	N419BN	2 Aug 73
964	20733	227	Braniff AW	N420BN	9 Aug 73
965	20734	227	Braniff AW	N421BN	13 Aug 73
966	20727	281	All Nippon	JA8348	17 Aug 73
967	20646	232	Delta AL	N464DA	10 Aug 73
968	20647	232	Delta AL	N465DA	22 Aug 73
969	20728	281	All Nippon	JA8349	24 Aug 73
970	20657	224	Continental AL	N24728	29 Aug 73
971	20743	232	Delta AL	N466DA	28 Aug 73
972	20744	232	Delta AL	N467DA	7 Sep 73
973	20735	227	Braniff AW	N422BN	10 Sep 73
974	20736	227	Braniff AW	N423BN	12 Sep 73
975	20710	264	Mexicana	XA-CUE	14 Sep 73
976	20737	227	Braniff AW	N424BN	20 Sep 73
977	20738	227	Braniff AW	N425BN	21 Sep 73
978	20658	224	Continental AL	N25729	24 Sep 73
979	20659	224	Continental AL	N29730	3 Oct 73
980	20745	232	Delta AL	N468DA	27 Sep 73
981	20746	232	Delta AL	N469DA	8 Oct 73
982	20772	227	Braniff AW	N426BN	8 Oct 73
983	20773	227	Braniff AW	N427BN	10 Oct 73
984	20765	2J4	Sterling AW	OY-SAS	23 Oct 73
985	20660	224	Continental AL	N66731	16 Oct 73
986	20780	264	Mexicana	XA-CUN	22 Oct 73
987	20747	232	Delta AL	N470DA	25 Oct 73
988	20748	232	Delta AL	N471DA	29 Oct 73
989	20549	277	Ansett AL	VH-RMV	15 Nov 73
990	20749	232	Delta AL	N472DA	5 Nov 73
991	20553	276	TAA	VH-TBH	18 Nov 73
992	20750	232	Delta AL	N473DA	16 Nov 73
993	20766	2J4	Sterling AW	OY-SAT	16 Nov 73
994	20823	225	Eastern AL	N8867E	28 Nov 73

Above:
State owned Trans Australia Airlines (renamed Australian Airlines in 1986 and purchased by Qantas during 1992) ordered its initial batch of 727-100s way back in 1962. The carrier's first long-bodied 200-series (VH-TBG — seen here on test from Seattle) was delivered in 1972, and remained in service until the whole 727 fleet was retired at the beginning of 1993.

Below:
Surprisingly enough, the only pure cargo versions of the 727 ever built at Renton were the 15 727-200Fs ordered by Federal Express. These aircraft had fewer emergency exits, no passenger windows, and were stripped of all the plumbing and wiring normally associated with passenger amenities. The cargo door was virtually identical to that on the 707-320C, and the cabin floor was strengthened to take heavier point loads. The first aircraft (N201FE — seen here) was delivered to the customer in April 1983.

Line No	Constrn No	Model No	First Operator	Delivery Registration	First flight	Line No	Constrn No	Model No	First Operator	Delivery Registration	First flight
995	20824	225	Eastern AL	N8869E	21 Nov 73	1067	20866	232	Delta AL	N486DA	3 Sep 74
996	20822	2H3	Tunis Air	TS-JHP	28 Nov 73	1068	20867	232	Delta AL	N487DA	6 Sep 74
997	20774	227	Braniff AW	N428BN	30 Nov 73	1069	20932	233	Air Canada	C-GAAA	16 Sep 74
998	20775	227	Braniff AW	N429BN	11 Dec 73	1070	20947	286	Iran Air	EP-IRS	12 Sep 74
999	20787	264	Mexicana	XA-DAT	15 Dec 73	1071	20933	233	Air Canada	C-GAAB	19 Sep 74
1000	20751	232	Delta AL	N474DA	18 Dec 73	1072	20662	224	Continental AL	N66733	21 Sep 74
1001	20752	232	Delta AL	N475DA	14 Dec 73	1073	20663	224	Continental AL	N66734	20 Sep 74
1002	20757	230	Lufthansa	D-ABQI	21 Dec 73	1074	20934	233	Air Canada	C-GAAC	2 Oct 74
1003	20811	256	Iberia	EC-CFA	21 Dec 73	1075	20955	206	Air Algerie	7T-VEH	27 Sep 74
1004	20812	256	Iberia	EC-CFB	11 Jan 74	1076	20935	233	Air Canada	C-GAAD	18 Oct 74
1005	20813	256	Iberia	EC-CFC	8 Jan 74	1077	20974	256	Iberia	EC-CID	11 Oct 74
1006	20814	256	Iberia	EC-CFD	11 Jan 74	1078	20936	233	Air Canada	C-GAAE	16 Oct 74
1007	20815	256	Iberia	EC-CFE	17 Jan 74	1079	20664	224	Continental AL	N66735	16 Oct 74
1008	20816	256	Iberia	EC-CCF	18 Jan 74	1080	20975	256	Iberia	EC-CIE	18 Oct 74
1009	20817	256	Iberia	EC-CFG	22 Jan 74	1081	20950	276	TAA	VH-TBK	22 Oct 74
1010	20818	256	Iberia	EC-CFH	25 Jan 74	1082	21021	2D3	Alia	JY-ADV	25 Oct 74
1011	20788	230	Lufthansa	D-ABRI	1 Feb 74	1083	20978	277	Ansett AL	VH-RMY	29 Oct 74
1012	20753	232	Delta AL	N476DA	1 Feb 74	1084	20948	2H3	Tunis Air	TS-JHQ	4 Nov 74
1013	20754	232	Delta AL	N477DA	4 Feb 74	1085	20980	2F2	THY	TC-JBF	31 Oct 74
1014	20755	232	Delta AL	N478DA	8 Feb 74	1086	20981	2F2	THY	TC-JBG	11 Nov 74
1015	20789	230	Lufthansa	D-ABSI	14 Feb 74	1087	20982	2F2	THY	TC-JBH	11 Nov 74
1016	20837	227	Braniff AW	N430BN	18 Feb 74	1088	20983	2F2	THY	TC-JBJ	18 Nov 74
1017	20838	227	Braniff AW	N431BN	20 Feb 74	1089	20903	230	Lufthansa	D-ABKE	21 Nov 74
1018	20819	256	Iberia	EC-CFI	26 Feb 74	1090	20904	230	Lufthansa	D-ABKF	5 Dec 74
1019	20820	256	Iberia	EC-CFJ	1 Mar 74	1091	20905	230	Lufthansa	D-ABKG	28 Jan 75
1020	20875	214	Pacific SW AL	N554PS	6 Mar 74	1092	20906	230	Lufthansa	D-ABKH	26 Feb 75
1021	20790	230	Condor	D-ABTI	5 Mar 74	1093	20918	230	Lufthansa	D-ABKJ	26 Mar 75
1022	20791	230	Lufthansa	D-ABVI	8 Mar 74	1094	21037	2H9	JAT	YU-AKE	10 Dec 74
1023	20792	230	Condor	D-ABWI	15 Mar 74	1095	21018	232	Delta AL	N488DA	17 Jan 75
1024	20868	247	Western AL	N2812W	20 Mar 74	1096	20972	282	TAP	CS-TBR	7 Jan 75
1025	20869	247	Western AL	N2813W	22 Mar 74	1097	21019	232	Delta AL	N489DA	14 Feb 75
1026	20876	281	All Nippon AW	JA8350	26 Mar 74	1098	20979	277	Ansett AL	VH-RMZ	3 Apr 75
1027	20554	276	TAA	VH-TBI	27 Mar 74	1099	20973	282	TAP	CS-TBS	14 Jan 75
1028	20756	232	Delta AL	N479DA	3 Apr 74	1100	21010	2L4	Am Capital Av	N111AK	7 Jan 75
1029	20877	281	All Nippon	JA8351	2 Apr 74	1101	20951	276	TAA	VH-TBL	4 Apr 75
1030	20550	277	Ansett AL	VH-RMW	1 Apr 74	1102	21020	232	Delta AL	N490DA	7 Apr 75
1031	20839	227	Braniff AW	N432BN	9 Apr 74	1103	20937	233	Air Canada	C-GAAF	21 Feb 75
1032	20870	247	Western AL	N2814W	11 Apr 74	1104	21041	227	Braniff AW	N434BN	24 Jan 75
1033	20879	2J7	Air Jamaica	N128NA	22 Apr 74	1105	20938	233	Air Canada	C-GAAG	3 Mar 75
1034	20878	281	All Nippon	JA8352	23 Apr 74	1106	21042	227	Braniff AW	N435BN	29 Jan 75
1035	20821	256	Iberia	EC-CFK	26 Apr 74	1107	21068	2B6	RAM	CN-CCW	5 Feb 75
1036	20840	227	Braniff AW	N433BN	30 Apr 74	1108	21050	2L5	Libyan Arab	5A-DIA	7 Feb 75
1037	20880	2J7	Air Jamaica	N129NA	2 May 74	1109	21051	2L5	Libyan Arab	5A-DIB	14 Feb 75
1038	20860	232	Delta AL	N480DA	7 May 74	1110	21052	2L5	Libyan Arab	5A-DIC	26 Feb 75
1039	20871	247	Western AL	N2815W	17 May 74	1111	21053	2D6	Air Algerie	7T-VEI	20 Feb 75
1040	20872	247	Western AL	N2816W	10 May 74	1112	20939	233	Air Canada	C-GAAH	24 Mar 75
1041	20861	232	Delta AL	N481DA	15 May 74	1113	21043	227	Braniff AW	N436BN	27 Feb 75
1042	20862	232	Delta AL	N482DA	24 May 74	1114	21078	286	Iran Air	EP-IRT	3 Mar 77
1043	20873	247	Western AL	N2817W	21 May 74	1115	21060	232	Delta AL	N491DA	21 Mar 75
1044	20930	2H9	JAT	YU-AKA	31 May 74	1116	21061	232	Delta AL	N492DA	12 Mar 75
1045	20931	2H9	JAT	YU-AKB	29 May 74	1117	21055	217	CP Air	C-GCPA	12 Mar 75
1046	20899	230	Lufthansa	D-ABKA	6 Jun 74	1118	21038	2H9	JAT	YU-AKF	14 Mar 75
1047	20894	264	Mexicana	XA-DUI	5 Jun 74	1119	21039	2H9	JAT	YU-AKG	19 Mar 75
1048	20945	286	Iran Air	EP-IRP	12 Jun 74	1120	20940	233	Air Canada	C-GAAI	31 Mar 75
1049	20895	264	Mexicana	XA-DUJ	11 Jun 74	1121	20984	223	American AL	N843AA	23 Mar 75
1050	20900	230	Lufthansa	D-ABKB	19 Jun 74	1122	21056	217	CP Air	C-GCPB	31 Mar 75
1051	20896	264	Mexicana	XA-DUK	18 Jun 74	1123	20985	223	American AL	N844AA	18 Apr 75
1052	20904	286	Iran Air	EP-IRR	24 Jun 74	1124	21082	2K3	Lloyd Aero	CP-1276	2 Apr 75
1053	20863	232	Delta AL	N483DA	26 Jun 74	1125	20986	223	American AL	N845AA	6 May 75
1054	20551	277	Ansett AL	VH-RMX	3 Jul 74	1126	20987	223	American AL	N846AA	7 May 75
1055	20885	203	Alia	JY-ADR	28 Jun 74	1127	21062	232	Delta AL	N493DA	11 Apr 75
1056	20555	276	TAA	VH-TBJ	12 Jul 74	1128	20941	233	Air Canada	C-GAAJ	28 Apr 75
1057	20874	247	Western AL	N2818W	16 Jul 74	1129	21036	2J1	Dominicana	HI-242	23 Apr 75
1058	20901	230	Lufthansa	D-ABKC	18 Jul 74	1130	20942	233	Air Canada	C-GAAK	5 May 75
1059	20902	230	Lufthansa	D-ABKD	23 Jul 74	1131	21079	286	Iran Air	EP-IRU	29 Apr 75
1060	20864	232	Delta AL	N484DA	8 Aug 74	1132	21044	227	Braniff AW	N437BN	3 May 75
1061	20886	2D3	Alia	JY-ADU	26 Jul 74	1133	21045	227	Braniff AW	N438BN	5 May 75
1062	20865	232	Delta AL	N485DA	16 Aug 74	1134	21091	2M1	Senegal Gov	6V-AEF	14 Jun 75
1063	20843	231	TWA	N54338	20 Aug 74	1135	21057	247	Western AL	N2819W	9 May 75
1064	20661	224	Continental AL	N66732	22 Aug 74	1136	21058	247	Western AL	N2820W	16 May 75
1065	20844	231	TWA	N54339	27 Aug 74	1137	21059	247	Western AL	N2821W	22 May 75
1066	20845	231	TWA	N54340	29 Aug 74	1138	21074	232	Delta AL	N494DA	29 May 75

Line No	Constrn No	Model No	First Operator	Delivery Registration	First flight
1139	21075	232	Delta AL	N495DA	28 May 75
1140	21076	232	Delta AL	N496DA	11 Jun 75
1141	20988	223	American AL	N847AA	4 Jun 75
1142	21040	2L8	Yugoslav Gov	14302	18 Jun 75
1143	21071	264	Mexicana	XA-FID	9 Jun 75
1144	20989	223	American AL	N848AA	13 Jun 75
1145	21072	264	Mexicana	XA-FIE	16 Jun 75
1146	21080	2L8	Yugoslav Gov	14301	14 Jul 75
1147	21077	232	Delta AL	N497DA	23 Jun 75
1148	21100	233	Air Canada	C-GAAL	23 Jul 75
1149	20665	224	Continental AL	N66736	18 Aug 75
1150	21101	233	Air Canada	C-GAAM	31 Jul 75
1151	20666	224	Continental AL	N93738	27 Aug 75
1152	21102	233	Air Canada	C-GAAN	25 Aug 75
1153	20667	224	Continental AL	N69739	26 Sep 75
1154	20668	224	Continental AL	N69740	3 Oct 75
1155	21142	232	Delta AL	N498DA	18 Aug 75
1156	21143	232	Delta AL	N499DA	21 Aug 75
1157	21144	232	Delta AL	N400DA	30 Jul 75
1158	21105	2J0	Air Jamaica	6Y-JMA	22 Aug 75
1159	21145	232	Delta AL	N401DA	25 Aug 75
1160	21106	2J0	Air Jamaica	6Y-JMB	9 Sep 75
1161	21146	232	Delta AL	N402DA	23 Sep 75
1162	21147	232	Delta AL	N403DA	30 Sep 75
1163	21148	232	Delta AL	N404DA	23 Oct 75
1164	21149	232	Delta AL	N405DA	17 Oct 75
1165	21150	232	Delta AL	N406DA	18 Nov 75
1166	21151	232	Delta AL	N407DA	25 Nov 75
1167	21118	227	Braniff AW	N439BN	24 Sep 75
1168	21154	251	NW Orient AL	N275US	5 Oct 75
1169	21155	251	NW Orient AL	N276US	16 Oct 75
1170	21156	251	NW Orient AL	N277US	22 Oct 75
1171	21179	2H3	Air Tunis	TS-JHR	28 Oct 75
1172	21107	2J0	Air Jamaica	6Y-JMC	31 Oct 75
1173	21157	251	NW Orient AL	N278US	7 Nov 75
1174	21108	2J0	Air Jamaica	6Y-JMD	11 Nov 75
1175	21119	227	Braniff AW	N440BN	19 Nov 75
1176	21113	230	Condor	D-ABKK	20 Nov 75
1177	21158	251	NW Orient AL	N279US	3 Dec 75
1178	21114	230	Condor	D-ABKL	5 Dec 75
1179	21159	251	NW Orient AL	N280US	6 Dec 75
1180	21160	251	NW Orient AL	N281US	13 Dec 75
1181	21161	251	NW Orient AL	N282US	7 Jan 76
1182	21152	232	Delta AL	N408DA	7 Jan 76
1183	21153	232	Delta AL	N409DA	19 Jan 76
1184	20990	223	American AL	N849AA	27 Apr 76
1185	20991	223	American AL	N850AA	26 Apr 76
1186	21197	270	Iraqi AW	YI-AGK	3 Feb 76
1187	20992	223	American AL	N851AA	29 Apr 76
1188	21203	294	Syrianair	YK-AGA	20 Feb 76
1189	20993	223	American AL	N852AA	5 May 76
1190	20994	223	American AL	N853AA	6 May 76
1191	21198	270	Iraqi AW	YI-AGL	26 Feb 76
1192	20995	223	American AL	N854AA	27 May 76
1193	20996	223	American AL	N855AA	4 Jun 76
1194	21204	294	Syrianair	YK-AGB	18 Mar 76
1195	20997	223	American AL	N856AA	10 Jun 76
1196	21242	227	Braniff AW	N441BN	31 Mar 76
1197	21243	227	Braniff AW	N442BN	8 Apr 76
1198	21205	294	Syrianair	YK-AGC	9 Apr 76
1199	21084	223	American AL	N857AA	13 Apr 76
1200	21085	223	American AL	N858AA	17 Apr 76
1201	21244	227	Braniff AW	N443BN	21 Apr 76
1202	21245	227	Braniff AW	N444BN	27 Apr 76
1203	21199	270	Iraqi AW	YI-AGM	7 May 76
1204	21210	2D6	Air Algerie	7T-VEM	13 May 76
1205	21222	232	Delta AL	N410DA	14 May 76
1206	21200	2M7	Hughes A'West	N721RW	27 May 76
1207	21223	232	Delta AL	N411DA	21 May 76
1208	21232	232	Delta AL	N412DA	15 Jul 76
1209	21234	2H3	Tunis Air	TS-JHS	8 Jun 76
1210	21235	2H3	Tunis Air	TS-JHT	11 Jul 76
1211	21233	232	Delta AL	N413DA	28 Jul 76
1212	21256	232	Delta AL	N414DA	13 Oct 76
1213	21229	2L5	Libyan Arab	5A-DID	2 Jul 76
1214	21257	232	Delta AL	N415DA	14 Oct 76
1215	21230	2L5	Libyan Arab	5A-DIE	16 Jul 76
1216	21246	227	Braniff AW	N445BN	17 Jul 76
1217	21247	227	Braniff AW	N446BN	22 Jul 76
1218	21248	227	Braniff AW	N447BN	14 Oct 76
1219	21249	227	Braniff AW	N448BN	18 Oct 76
1220	21201	2M7	Hughes A'West	N722RW	19 Oct 76
1221	21202	2M7	Hughes A'West	N723RW	20 Nov 76
1222	21260	2F2	THY	TC-JBM	9 Sep 76
1223	21258	232	Delta AL	N416DA	21 Sep 76
1224	21259	232	Delta AL	N417DA	24 Nov 76
1225	21265	243	Alitalia	I-DIRA	24 Sep 76
1226	21265	243	Alitalia	I-DIRI	4 Oct 76
1227	21266	243	Alitalia	I-DIRO	7 Oct 76
1228	21267	243	Alitalia	I-DIRU	8 Dec 76
1229	21268	243	Alitalia	I-DIRB	9 Dec 76
1230	21269	243	Alitalia	I-DIRC	1 Nov 76
1231	21270	243	Alitalia	I-DIRJ	4 Nov 76
1232	21171	276	TAA	VH-TBM	4 Nov 76
1233	21284	2D6	Air Algerie	7T-VEP	10 Nov 76
1234	21288	225	Eastern AL	N8870Z	16 Nov 76
1235	21289	225	Eastern AL	N8871Z	22 Nov 76
1236	21297	2B6	RAM	CN-RMO	24 Nov 76
1237	21178	277	Ansett AL	VH-RMK	13 Dec 76
1238	21290	225	Eastern AL	N8872Z	8 Dec 76
1239	21291	225	Eastern AL	N8873Z	8 Dec 76
1240	21292	225	Eastern AL	N8874Z	11 Dec 76
1241	21293	225	Eastern AL	N8875Z	16 Dec 76
1242	21271	232	Delta AL	N418DA	14 Jan 77
1243	21272	232	Delta AL	N419DA	19 Jan 77
1244	21273	232	Delta AL	N420DA	21 Jan 77
1245	21274	232	Delta AL	N421DA	28 Jan 77
1246	21298	2B6	RAM	CN-RMP	4 Feb 77
1247	21299	2B6	RAM	CN-RMQ	2 Mar 77
1248	21086	223	American AL	N859AA	15 Feb 77
1249	21327	247	Western AL	N2822W	18 Feb 77
1250	21087	223	American AL	N860AA	24 Feb 77
1251	21328	247	Western AL	N2823W	25 Feb 77
1252	21318	2H3	Tunis Air	TS-JHU	8 Mar 77
1253	21341	2A1	VASP	PP-SNE	17 Mar 77
1254	21329	247	Western AL	N2824W	15 Mar 77
1255	21088	223	American AL	N861AA	21 Mar 77
1256	21342	2A1	VASP	PP-SNF	29 Mar 77
1257	21332	2L5	Libyan Arab	5A-DIF	5 Apr 77
1258	21363	227	Braniff AW	N449BN	11 Apr 77
1259	21333	2L5	Libyan Arab	5A-DIG	15 Apr 77
1260	21330	247	Western AL	N2825W	18 Apr 77
1261	21364	227	Braniff AW	N450BN	6 May 77
1262	21303	232	Delta AL	N501DA	23 Apr 77
1263	21089	223	American AL	N862AA	4 May 77
1264	21304	232	Delta AL	N502DA	3 May 77
1265	21322	251	NW Orient AL	N283US	12 May 77
1266	21331	247	Western AL	N2826W	11 May 77
1267	21090	223	American AL	N863AA	19 May 77
1268	21305	232	Delta AL	N503DA	20 May 77
1269	21319	2H3	Tunis Air	TS-JHV	31 May 77
1270	21306	232	Delta AL	N504DA	3 Jun 77
1271	21320	2H3	Tunis Air	TS-JHW	3 Jun 77
1272	21307	232	Delta AL	N505DA	13 Jun 77
1273	21365	227	Braniff AW	N451BN	13 Jun 77
1274	21366	227	Braniff AW	N452BN	24 Jun 77
1275	21369	223	American AL	N864AA	17 Jun 77
1276	21370	223	American AL	N865AA	29 Jun 77
1277	21371	223	American AL	N866AA	1 Jul 77
1278	21372	223	American AL	N867AA	8 Jul 77
1279	21373	223	American AL	N868AA	8 Jul 77
1280	21374	223	American AL	N869AA	13 Jul 77
1281	21394	227	Braniff AW	N453BN	15 Jul 77
1282	21347	212	Singapore AL	9V-SGA	15 Jul 77

Line No	Constrn No	Model No	First Operator	Delivery Registration	First flight
1283	21395	227	Braniff AW	N454BN	24 Jul 77
1284	21323	251	NW Orient AL	N284US	29 Jul 77
1285	21426	2F9	Nigerian AW	5N-ANP	9 Aug 77
1286	21324	251	NW Orient AL	N285US	11 Aug 77
1287	21438	212	Singapore AL	9V-SGB	14 Sep 77
1288	21325	251	NW Orient AL	N286US	19 Aug 77
1289	21349	212	Singapore AL	9V-SGC	3 Oct 77
1290	21375	251	NW Orient AL	N287US	26 Aug 77
1291	21427	2F9	Nigerian AW	5N-ANQ	31 Aug 77
1292	21308	232	Delta AL	N506DA	7 Sep 77
1293	21376	251	NW Orient AL	N288US	7 Sep 77
1294	21309	232	Delta AL	N507DA	15 Sep 77
1295	21377	251	NW Orient AL	N289US	14 Sep 77
1296	21398	222	United AL	N7251U	29 Sep 77
1297	21378	251	NW Orient AL	N290US	21 Sep 77
1298	21310	232	Delta AL	N508DA	29 Sep 77
1299	21379	251	NW Orient AL	N291US	27 Sep 77
1300	21311	232	Delta AL	N509DA	11 Oct 77
1301	21438	2J4	Sterling AW	OY-SBC	21 Oct 77
1302	21457	2M7	Hughes A'West	N724RW	19 Oct 77
1303	21399	222	United AL	N7252U	27 Oct 77
1304	21382	223	American AL	N870AA	4 Nov 77
1305	21392	247	Western AL	N2827W	2 Dec 77
1306	21449	225	Eastern AL	N8876Z	11 Nov 77
1307	21393	247	Western AL	N2828W	13 Dec 77
1308	21450	225	Eastern AL	N8877Z	30 Nov 77
1309	21400	222	United AL	N7253U	23 Dec 77
1310	21451	225	Eastern AL	N8878Z	12 Jan 78
1311	21401	222	United AL	N7254U	11 Jan 78
1312	21452	225	Eastern AL	N8879Z	19 Jan 78
1313	21402	222	United AL	N7255U	16 Jan 78
1314	21453	225	Eastern AL	N8880Z	26 Jan 78
1315	21403	222	United AL	N7256U	17 Jan 78
1316	21455	281	All Nippon AW	JA8353	28 Jan 78
1317	21503	251	NW Orient AL	N292US	2 Feb 78
1318	21456	281	All Nippon	JA8354	2 Feb 78
1319	21504	251	NW Orient AL	N293US	8 Feb 78
1320	21343	2A1	Avianca	HK-2151	13 Feb 78
1321	21404	222	United AL	N7257U	20 Feb 78
1322	21344	2A1	Avianca	HK-2152	22 Sep 78
1323	21405	222	United AL	N7258U	24 Feb 78
1324	21383	223	American AL	N871AA	24 Feb 78
1325	21406	222	United AL	N7259U	3 Mar 78
1326	21442	230	Lufthansa	D-ABKM	3 Mar 78
1327	21458	212	Singapore AL	9V-SGD	13 Mar 78
1328	21384	223	American AL	N872AA	8 Mar 78
1329	21459	212	Singapore AL	9V-SGE	11 Mar 78
1330	21312	232	Delta AL	N510DA	22 Mar 78
1331	21385	223	American AL	N873AA	15 Mar 78
1332	21407	222	United AL	N7260U	28 Mar 78
1333	21386	223	American AL	N874AA	4 Apr 78
1334	21408	222	United AL	N7261U	4 Apr 78
1335	21387	223	American AL	N875AA	4 Apr 78
1336	21409	222	United AL	N7262U	11 Apr 78
1337	21461	227	Braniff AW	N455BN	18 Apr 78
1338	21481	247	Western AL	N2829W	20 Apr 78
1339	21502	2M7	Hughes A'West	N725RW	20 Apr 78
1340	21460	212	Singapore AL	9V-SGF	18 Apr 78
1341	21482	247	Western AL	N830WA	24 Apr 78
1342	21462	227	Braniff AW	N456BN	1 May 78
1343	21512	214	Pacific SW AL	N555PS	4 May 78
1344	21410	222	United AL	N7263U	3 May 78
1345	21388	223	American AL	N876AA	5 May 78
1346	21411	222	United AL	N7264U	8 May 78
1347	21313	232	Delta AL	N511DA	15 May 78
1348	21412	222	United AL	N7265U	17 May 78
1349	21389	223	American AL	N877AA	16 May 78
1350	21483	247	Western AL	N831WA	19 May 78
1351	21413	222	United AL	N7266U	24 May 78
1352	21480	277	Ansett AL	VH-RML	23 May 78
1353	21463	227	Braniff AW	N457BN	2 Jun 78
1354	21414	222	United AL	N7267U	31 May 78
1355	21464	227	Braniff AW	N458BN	6 Jun 78
1356	21415	222	United AL	N7268U	6 Jun 78
1357	21479	276	TAA	VH-TBN	9 Jun 78
1358	21314	232	Delta AL	N512DA	9 Jun 78
1359	21510	290	Alaska AL	N290AS	14 Jun 78
1360	21315	232	Delta AL	N513DA	21 Jun 78
1361	21390	223	American AL	N878AA	20 Jun 78
1362	21484	247	Western AL	N282WA	28 Jun 78
1363	21465	227	Braniff AW	N459BN	30 Jun 78
1364	21485	247	Western AL	N283WA	26 Jun 78
1365	21513	214	Pacific SW AL	N556PS	7 Jul 78
1366	21416	222	United AL	N7269U	6 Jul 78
1367	21391	223	American AL	N879AA	13 Jul 78
1368	21417	222	United AL	N7270U	12 Jul 78
1369	21609	256	Iberia	EC-DCC	19 Jul 78
1370	21418	222	United AL	N7271U	18 Jul 78
1371	21539	2L5	Libyan Arab AL	5A-DIH	19 Jul 78
1372	21466	227	Braniff AW	N460BN	28 Jul 78
1373	21494	2K3	Lloyd Aero	CP-1366	24 Jul 78
1374	21430	232	Delta AL	N514DA	27 Jul 78
1375	21419	222	United AL	N7272U	9 Aug 78
1376	21431	232	Delta AL	N515DA	4 Aug 78
1377	21420	222	United AL	N7273U	10 Aug 78
1378	21474	281	All Nippon AW	JA8355	9 Aug 78
1379	21577	264	Mexicana	XA-HOH	11 Aug 78
1380	21610	256	Iberia	EC-DCD	16 Aug 78
1381	21432	232	Delta AL	N516DA	22 Aug 78
1382	21611	256	Iberia	EC-DCE	21 Aug 78
1383	21421	222	United AL	N7274U	25 Aug 78
1384	21433	232	Delta AL	N517DA	24 Aug 78
1385	21422	222	United AL	N7275U	31 Aug 78
1386	21540	2L5	Libyan Arab AL	5A-DII	29 Aug 78
1387	21423	222	United AL	N7276U	6 Sep 78
1388	21488	227	Braniff AW	N461BN	11 Sep 78
1389	21603	2F2	THY	TC-JBR	8 Sep 78
1390	21489	227	Braniff AW	N462BN	18 Sep 78
1391	21505	251	NW Orient AL	N294US	12 Sep 78
1392	21506	251	NW Orient AL	N295US	13 Sep 78
1393	21424	222	United AL	N7277U	15 Sep 78
1394	21661	243	Alitalia	I-DIRD	25 Sep 78
1395	21425	222	United AL	N7278U	21 Sep 78
1396	21490	227	Braniff AW	N463BN	28 Sep 78
1397	21557	222	United AL	N7279U	3 Oct 78
1398	21469	232	Delta AL	N518DA	26 Sep 78
1399	21558	222	United AL	N7280U	6 Oct 78
1400	21470	232	Delta AL	N519DA	4 Oct 78
1401	21559	222	United AL	N7281U	11 Oct 78
1402	21491	227	Braniff AW	N464BN	17 Oct 78
1403	21495	2K3	Lloyd Aero	CP-1367	10 Oct 78
1404	21618	230	Lufthansa	D-ABKN	13 Oct 78
1405	21560	222	United AL	N7282U	19 Oct 78
1406	21595	2P1	State of Qatar	A7-AAB	9 Jan 79
1407	21619	230	Lufthansa	D-ABKP	20 Oct 78
1408	21561	222	United AL	N7283U	24 Oct 78
1409	21578	225	Eastern AL	N8881Z	1 Nov 78
1410	21562	222	United AL	N7284U	30 Oct 78
1411	21471	232	Delta AL	N520DA	27 Oct 78
1412	21579	225	Eastern AL	N8882Z	8 Nov 78
1413	21472	232	Delta AL	N521DA	4 Nov 78
1414	21636	2R1	Cameroon Gov	TJ-AAM	8 Nov 78
1415	21688	287	Aero Argentinas	LV-MIM	10 Nov 78
1416	21617	264	Mexicana	XA-HON	16 Nov 78
1417	21676	2J4	Sterling AW	OY-SBD	15 Nov 78
1418	21563	222	United AL	N7285U	17 Nov 78
1419	21620	230	Lufthansa	D-ABKQ	28 Nov 78
1420	21564	222	United AL	N7286U	22 Nov 78
1421	21662	243	Alitalia	I-DIRF	1 Dec 78
1422	21582	232	Delta AL	N522DA	30 Nov 78
1423	21583	232	Delta AL	N523DA	6 Dec 78
1424	21565	222	United AL	N7287U	7 Dec 78
1425	21621	230	Lufthansa	D-ABKR	11 Dec 78
1426	21608	2Q8	Pacific SW AL	N791L	9 Jan 79

Above:
N724RW was the first 727 supplied to Aerolineas Argentinas. First flown on 19 October 1977, it was delivered to the airline on 1 December that year. The registration number belongs to Hughes Airwest, which leased the aircraft to the Argentinian airline. *Boeing*

Below:
The first of Hapag-Lloyd's three 727-200s was line number 1551. Delivered to the Bremen-based operator of charter and inclusive tour flights, the aircraft first flew on 13 November 1979. It is pictured here on test flight prior to being delivered to the airline. *Boeing*

Line No	Constrn No	Model No	First Operator	Delivery Registration	First flight
1427	21689	287	Aero Argentinas	LV-MIN	12 Dec 78
1428	21566	222	United AL	N7288U	14 Dec 78
1429	21637	264	Mexicana	XA-HOV	15 Dec 78
1430	21567	222	United AL	N7289U	20 Dec 78
1431	21622	230	Lufthansa	D-ABKS	3 Jan 79
1432	21568	222	United AL	N7290U	21 Dec 78
1433	21623	230	Lufthansa	D-ABKT	10 Jan 79
1434	21646	276	TAA	VH-TBO	10 Jan 79
1435	21580	225	Eastern AL	N8883Z	16 Jan 79
1436	21647	277	Ansett AL	VH-RMM	12 Jan 79
1437	21581	225	Eastern AL	N8884Z	22 Jan 79
1438	21663	243	Alitalia	I-DIRG	18 Jan 79
1439	21511	290	Alaska AL	N291AS	22 Jan 79
1440	21492	227	Braniff AW	N465BN	30 Jan 78
1441	21569	222	United AL	N7291U	25 Jan 79
1442	21493	227	Braniff AW	N466BN	2 Feb 79
1443	21570	222	United AL	N7292U	30 Jan 79
1444	21529	227	Braniff AW	N467BN	8 Feb 79
1445	21571	222	United AL	N7293U	5 Feb 79
1446	21530	227	Braniff AW	N468BN	14 Feb 79
1447	21572	222	United AL	N7294U	8 Feb 79
1448	21664	243	Alitalia	I-DIRL	12 Feb 79
1449	21573	222	United AL	N7295U	14 Feb 79
1450	21531	227	Braniff AW	N469BN	21 Feb 79
1451	21574	222	United AL	N7296U	19 Feb 79
1452	21655	2M7	Hughes A'West	N726RW	23 Feb 79
1453	21532	227	Braniff AW	N470BN	1 Mar 79
1454	21628	231	TWA	N54341	22 Feb 79
1455	21656	2M7	Hughes Airwest	N727RW	2 Mar 79
1456	21629	231	TWA	M54342	2 Mar 79
1457	21638	264	Mexicana	XA-HOX	9 Mar 79
1458	21630	231	TWA	N54343	8 Mar 79
1459	21519	223	American AL	N880AA	7 Mar 79
1460	21631	231	TWA	N54344	13 Mar 79
1461	21520	223	American AL	N881AA	20 Mar 79
1462	21632	231	TWA	N54345	19 Mar 79
1463	21521	223	American AL	N882AA	22 Mar 79
1464	21633	231	TWA	N64346	22 Mar 79
1465	21522	223	American AL	N883AA	29 Mar 79
1466	21634	231	TWA	N64347	28 Mar 79
1467	21523	223	American AL	N884AA	3 Apr 79
1468	21624	233	Air Canada	C-GAAO	2 Apr 79
1469	21690	287	Aero Argentinas	LV-MIO	9 Apr 79
1470	21625	233	Air Canada	C-GAAP	6 Apr 79
1471	21697	247	Western AL	N284WA	12 Apr 79
1472	21626	233	Air Canada	C-GAAQ	11 Apr 79
1473	21524	223	American AL	N885AA	18 Apr 79
1474	21698	247	Western AL	N286WA	16 Apr 79
1475	21525	223	American AL	N886AA	23 Apr 79
1476	21526	223	American AL	N887AA	19 Apr 79
1477	21527	223	American AL	N889AA	27 Apr 79
1478	21584	232	Delta AL	N524DA	26 Apr 79
1479	21585	232	Delta AL	N525DA	1 May 79
1480	21691	214	Pacific SW AL	N557PS	4 May 79
1481	21695	277	Ansett AL	VH-RMN	8 May 79
1482	21692	214	Pacific SW AL	N558PS	7 May 79
1483	21696	276	TAA	VH-TBP	11 May 79
1484	21669	227	Braniff AW	N471BN	16 May 79
1485	21699	247	Western AL	N287WA	14 May 79
1486	21670	227	Braniff AW	N472BN	21 May 79
1487	21777	256	Iberia	EC-DDU	18 May 79
1488	21586	232	Delta AL	N526DA	25 May 79
1489	21700	247	Western AL	N288WA	23 May 79
1490	21778	256	Iberia	EC-DDV	31 May 79
1491	21741	2M7	Hughes Airwest	N728RW	25 May 79
1492	21587	232	Delta AL	N527DA	5 Jun 79
1493	21701	247	Western AL	N289WA	1 Jun 79
1494	21949	282	TAP	CS-TBW	11 Jun 79
1495	21788	251	NW Orient AL	N296US	6 Jun 79
1496	21789	251	NW Orient AL	N297US	8 Jun 79
1497	21836	264	Mexicana	XA-IEU	13 Jun 79
1498	21779	256	Iberia	EC-DDX	20 Jun 79
1499	21780	256	Iberia	EC-DDY	18 Jun 79
1500	21892	222	United AL	N7297U	19 Jun 79
1501	21781	256	Iberia	EC-DDZ	22 Jun 79
1502	21945	212	Singapore AL	9V-SGG	27 Jun 79
1503	21893	222	United AL	N7298U	2 Jul 79
1504	21946	212	Singapore AL	9V-SGH	6 Jul 79
1505	21894	222	United AL	N7299U	11 Jul 79
1506	21947	212	Singapore AL	9V-SGI	6 Jul 79
1507	21895	222	United AL	N7441U	16 Jul 79
1508	21930	2Q9	Avianca	N200AV	11 Jul 79
1509	21826	2Q8	Western AL	N831L	13 Jul 79
1510	21948	212	Singapore AL	9V-SGJ	17 Jul 79
1511	21896	222	United AL	N7442U	24 Jul 79
1512	21842	2N8	Yemen AW	4W-ACJ	20 Jul 79
1513	21897	222	United AL	N7443U	27 Jul 79
1514	21742	2M7	Hughes Airwest	N729RW	26 Jul 79
1515	21898	222	United AL	N7444U	1 Aug 79
1516	21953	2B7	Allegheny AL	N760AL	31 Jul 79
1517	21899	222	United AL	N7445U	7 Aug 79
1518	21844	2N8	Yemen AW	4W-ACF	6 Aug 79
1519	21900	222	United AL	N7446U	10 Aug 79
1520	21978	260	Ethiopian AL	ET-AHL	24 Aug 79
1521	21901	222	United AL	N7447U	30 Aug 79
1522	21702	232	Delta AL	N528DA	29 Aug 79
1523	21671	233	Air Canada	C-GAAR	6 Sep 79
1524	21902	222	United AL	N7448U	10 Sep 79
1525	21954	2B7	Allegheny AL	N762AL	4 Sep 79
1526	21903	222	United AL	N7449U	13 Sep 79
1527	21849	2D4	Pan American	N361PA	12 Sep 79
1528	21904	222	United AL	N7450U	18 Sep 79
1529	21845	2N8	Yemen AW	4W-ACG	17 Sep 79
1530	21905	222	United AL	N7451U	21 Sep 79
1531	21931	2Q9	Avianca	N202AV	20 Sep 79
1532	21854	225	Eastern AL	N8885Z	28 Sep 79
1533	21958	214	Pacific SW AL	N559PS	25 Sep 79
1534	21979	260	Ethiopian AL	ET-AHM	28 Sep 79
1535	21855	225	Eastern AL	N8886Z	9 Oct 79
1536	21850	2D4	Pan American	N326PA	3 Oct 79
1537	21856	225	Eastern AL	N8887Z	11 Oct 79
1538	21672	233	Air Canada	C-GAAS	9 Oct 79
1539	21857	225	Eastern AL	N8888Z	17 Oct 79
1540	21971	2Q6	LACSA	N1279E	12 Oct 79
1541	21673	233	Air Canada	C-GAAT	16 Oct 79
1542	21858	225	Eastern AL	N8889Z	23 Oct 79
1543	21674	233	Air Canada	C-GAAU	19 Oct 79
1544	21859	225	Eastern AL	N8890Z	30 Oct 79
1545	21837	264	Mexicana	XA-MEB	25 Oct 79
1546	21860	225	Eastern AL	N8891Z	1 Nov 79
1547	21838	264	Mexicana	XA-MEC	29 Oct 79
1548	21906	222	United AL	N7452U	5 Nov 79
1549	21846	2N8	Yemen AW	4W-ACH	2 Nov 79
1550	21703	232	Delta AL	N529DA	6 Nov 79
1551	21851	2K5	Hapag Lloyd	D-AHLT	13 Nov 79
1552	21813	232	Delta AL	N530DA	9 Nov 79
1553	21852	2K5	Hapag Lloyd	D-AHLU	19 Nov 79
1554	21861	225	Eastern AL	N8892Z	21 Nov 79
1555	21675	233	Air Canada	C-GAAV	19 Nov 79
1556	21814	232	Delta AL	N531DA	28 Nov 79
1557	21847	2N8	Yemen AW	4W-ACI	27 Nov 79
1558	21907	222	United AL	N7453U	4 Dec 79
1559	22043	294	AVENSA	YV-74C	29 Nov 79
1560	21908	222	United AL	N7454U	7 Dec 79
1561	22044	294	AVENSA	YV-75C	7 Dec 79
1562	21909	222	United AL	N7455U	13 Dec 79
1563	21967	231	TWA	N54348	11 Dec 79
1564	22017	276	TAA	VH-TBQ	13 Dec 79
1565	21968	231	TWA	N54349	17 Dec 79
1566	22016	277	Ansett AL	VH-RMO	2 Jan 80
1567	21969	231	TWA	N54350	20 Dec 79
1568	22052	243	Alitalia	I-DIRM	7 Jan 80
1569	21983	231	TWA	N54351	4 Jan 80
1570	21910	222	United AL	N7456U	10 Jan 80

Line No	Constrn No	Model No	First Operator	Delivery Registration	First flight
1571	21996	227	Braniff AW	N473BN	12 Jan 80
1572	21911	222	United AL	N7457U	21 Feb 80
1573	21997	227	Braniff AW	N474BN	17 Jan 80
1574	21984	231	TWA	N54352	17 Jan 80
1575	21912	222	United AL	N7458U	15 Feb 80
1576	21985	231	TWA	N54353	22 Jan 80
1577	21998	227	Braniff AW	N475BN	28 Jan 80
1578	22025	233	Air Canada	C-GAAW	28 Jan 80
1579	21950	282	TAP	CS-TBX	29 Jan 80
1580	21986	231	TWA	N54354	31 Jan 80
1581	21999	227	Braniff AW	N476BN	8 Feb 80
1582	21987	231	TWA	N84355	6 Feb 80
1583	22000	227	Braniff AW	N477BN	11 Feb 80
1584	22019	257	Republic AL	N715RC	11 Feb 80
1585	22001	227	Braniff AW	N478BN	19 Feb 80
1586	21988	231	TWA	N84356	15 Feb 80
1587	22108	247	Western AL	N290WA	22 Feb 80
1588	22079	2J4	Sterling AW	OY-SBE	21 Feb 80
1589	22109	247	Western AL	N291WA	26 Feb 80
1590	21989	231	TWA	N84357	27 Feb 80
1591	21823	2M7	Hughes A'West	N730RW	27 Feb 80
1592	22020	2S7	Republic AL	N712RC	5 Mar 80
1593	21913	222	United AL	N7459U	10 Mar 80
1594	22081	228	Air France	F-GCDA	7 Mar 80
1595	21824	2M7	Hughes A'West	N740RW	13 Mar 80
1596	22306	233	Air Canada	C-GAAX	11 Mar 80
1597	21914	222	United AL	N7460U	18 Mar 80
1598	22080	2J4	Sterling AW	OY-SBF	19 Mar 80
1599	22152	251	NW Orient AL	N298US	15 Mar 80
1600	22037	233	Air Canada	C-GAAY	20 Mar 80
1601	22153	251	NW Orient AL	N299US	26 Mar 80
1602	22045	232	Delta AL	N532DA	31 Mar 80
1603	22082	228	Air France	F-GCDB	27 Mar 80
1604	22046	232	Delta AL	N533DA	3 Apr 80
1605	22083	228	Air France	F-GCDC	8 Apr 80
1606	22047	232	Delta AL	N534DA	4 Apr 80
1607	22156	264	Mexicana	XA-MED	4 Apr 80
1608	22048	232	Delta AL	N535DA	9 Apr 80
1609	21915	222	United AL	N7461U	10 Apr 80
1610	22049	232	Delta AL	N536DA	15 Apr 80
1611	21916	222	United AL	N7462U	21 Apr 80
1612	22038	233	Air Canada	C-GAAZ	24 Apr 80
1613	22110	247	Western AL	N292WA	22 Apr 80
1614	22039	233	Air Canada	C-GYNA	29 Apr 80
1615	22111	247	Western AL	N293WA	25 Apr 80
1616	21917	222	United AL	N7463U	30 Apr 80
1617	22021	257	Republic AL	N716RC	6 May 80
1618	22112	247	Western AL	N294WA	5 May 80
1619	22157	264	Mexicana	XA-MEE	8 May 80
1620	22053	243	Alitalia	I-DIRN	3 May 80
1621	22146	290	Alaska AL	N294AS	9 May 80
1622	22295	208	Icelandair	TF-FLI	15 May 80
1623	22147	290	Alaska AL	N295AS	14 May 80
1624	22073	232	Delta AL	N537DA	20 May 80
1625	21918	222	United AL	N7464U	28 May 80
1626	22040	233	Air Canada	C-GYNB	23 May 80
1627	22002	227	Braniff AW	N479BN	3 Jun 80
1628	22041	233	Air Canada	C-GYNC	29 May 80
1629	22003	227	Air Florida	N271AF	6 Jun 80
1630	22042	233	Air Canada	C-GYND	4 Jun 80
1631	22004	227	Air Florida	N272AF	11 Jun 80
1632	21919	222	United AL	N7465U	16 Jun 80
1633	22377	2B6	RAM	CN-RMR	11 Jun 80
1634	21920	222	United AL	N7466U	19 Jun 80
1635	22165	243	Alitalia	I-DIRP	19 Jun 80
1636	22006	223	American AL	N890AA	18 Jun 80
1637	21972	2Q6	LACSA	N1280E	27 Jun 80
1638	22084	228	Air France	F-GCDD	24 Jun 80
1639	21921	222	United AL	N7467U	2 Jul 80
1640	21853	2K5	Hapag Lloyd	D-AHLV	27 Jun 80
1641	22268	2D3	Alia	JY-AFT	3 Jul 80
1642	22158	264	Mexicana	XA-MEF	3 Jul 80
1643	22007	223	American AL	N891AA	11 Jul 80
1644	22078	2T3	TAME (FAE078)	HC-BHM	28 Aug 80
1645	22154	251	NW Orient AL	N201US	16 Jul 80
1646	22008	223	American AL	N892AA	15 Jul 80
1647	22261	270	Iraqi AW	YI-AGQ	5 Aug 80
1648	22155	251	NW Orient AL	N202US	24 Jul 80
1649	22009	223	American AL	N893AA	29 Jul 80
1650	22010	223	American AL	N894AA	7 Aug 80
1651	22005	227	Air Florida	N273AF	14 Aug 80
1652	22359	269	Kuwait AW	9K-AFA	14 Aug 80
1653	22011	223	American AL	N895AA	19 Aug 80
1654	22344	257	Republic AL	N718RC	18 Aug 80
1655	22012	223	American AL	N896AA	18 Aug 80
1656	22074	232	Delta AL	N538DA	21 Aug 80
1657	22362	2U5	Jordanian Gov	JY-HNH	28 Aug 80
1658	22432	225	Eastern AL	N801EA	2 Sep 80
1659	22013	223	American AL	N897AA	28 Aug 80
1660	22068	277	Ansett AL	VH-RMP	2 Sep 80
1661	22069	276	TAA	VH-TBR	6 Sep 80
1662	22372	2D6	Air Algerie	7T-VET	9 Sep 80
1663	22014	223	American AL	N898AA	9 Sep 80
1664	22373	2D6	Air Algerie	7T-VEU	13 Sep 80
1665	22085	228	Air France	F-GCDE	15 Sep 80
1666	22015	223	American AL	N899AA	22 Sep 80
1667	22385	232	Delta AL	N539DA	19 Sep 80
1668	22433	225	Eastern AL	N802EA	29 Sep 80
1669	22386	232	Delta AL	N540DA	24 Sep 80
1670	22360	269	Kuwait AW	9K-AFB	26 Sep 80
1671	22434	225	Eastern AL	N803EA	17 Oct 80
1672	22387	232	Delta AL	N541DA	30 Sep 80
1673	21345	2A1	VASP	PP-SNG	7 Oct 80
1674	22435	225	Eastern AL	N804EA	20 Oct 80
1675	21436	2A1	VASP	PP-SNH	7 Oct 80
1676	22409	264	Mexicana	XA-MEH	10 Oct 80
1677	22436	225	Eastern AL	N805EA	3 Nov 80
1678	22410	264	Mexicana	XA-MEI	14 Oct 80
1679	21600	2A1	VASP	PP-SNI	23 Oct 80
1680	21951	2M7	Republic AL	N741RW	28 Oct 80
1681	22393	2H9	JAT	YU-AKI	23 Oct 80
1682	22437	225	Eastern AL	N806EA	6 Nov 80
1683	22424	2Q4	Mexicana	XA-MEQ	28 Oct 80
1684	22250	224	Continental AL	N69741	30 Oct 80
1685	22438	225	Eastern AL	N807EA	7 Nov 80
1686	22262	270	Iraqi AW	YI-AGR	5 Nov 80
1687	22251	224	Continental AL	N69742	11 Nov 80
1688	22474	259	Avianca	N203AV	11 Nov 80
1689	22439	225	Eastern AL	N808EA	18 Nov 80
1690	22475	259	Avianca	N204AV	14 Nov 80
1691	22394	2H9	JAT	YU-AKJ	17 Nov 80
1692	22440	225	Eastern AL	N809EA	21 Nov 80
1693	21952	2N7	Republic AL	N742RW	3 Dec 80
1694	21601	2A1	VASP	PP-SNJ	25 Nov 80
1695	22441	225	Eastern AL	N810EA	3 Dec 80
1696	22441	264	Mexicana	XA-MEJ	3 Dec 80
1697	22252	224	Continental AL	N79743	9 Dec 80
1698	22425	2Q4	Mexicana	XA-MER	8 Dec 80
1699	22345	233	Air Canada	C-GYNE	9 Dec 80
1700	22543	251	NW Orient AL	N203US	11 Dec 80
1701	22269	2D3	Alia	JY-AFU	18 Dec 80
1702	22253	224	Continental AL	N79744	23 Dec 80
1703	22544	251	NW Orient AL	N204US	18 Dec 80
1704	22346	233	Air Canada	C-GYNF	8 Jan 81
1705	22391	232	Delta AL	N542DA	6 Jan 81
1706	22091	227	Air Florida	N274AF	15 Jan 81
1707	22392	232	Delta AL	N543DA	8 Jan 81
1708	22347	233	Air Canada	C-GYNG	16 Jan 81
1709	22270	2D3	Alia	JY-AFV	15 Jan 81
1710	22287	228	Air France	F-GCDF	20 Jan 81
1711	22374	2D6	Air Algerie	7T-VEV	20 Jan 81
1712	22288	228	Air France	F-GCDG	22 Jan 81
1713	22271	2D3	Alia	JY-AFW	28 Jan 81
1714	22348	233	Air Canada	C-GYNH	3 Feb 81

Above:
This small celebration for the 1,600th 727 (C-GAAY) was photographed in April 1980 — just 16 ¹/₂ years after the first delivery to United Airlines. By this time, the aircraft were so numerous that 320 of them were airbourne somewhere in the world during every second of every day; more than 90 airlines had ordered one or other of the

various models, and 1.3 billion passengers had already paid to fly on them.

Below:
Line number 1706 was represented by a 227 for Air Florida. Registered N274AF, it flew first on 15 January 1981. *Boeing*

Line No	Constrn No	Model No	First Operator	Delivery Registration	First flight	Line No	Constrn No	Model No	First Operator	Delivery Registration	First flight
1715	22430	282	TAP	CS-TBY	30 Jan 81	1774	22536	221	Pan American	N364PA	26 Aug 81
1716	22361	269	Kuwait AW	9K-AFC	6 Feb 81	1775	22553	225	Eastern AL	N816EA	31 Aug 81
1717	22162	2B7	US Air	N770AL	12 Feb 81	1776	22662	264	Mexicana	XA-MXB	31 Aug 81
1718	22092	227	Air Florida	N725AF	9 Feb 81	1777	22604	287	Aero Argentinas	LV-OLO	11 Sep 81
1719	22289	228	Air France	F-GCDH	16 Feb 81	1778	22663	264	Mexicana	XA-MXC	17 Sep 81
1720	22412	264	Mexicana	XA-MEK	20 Feb 81	1779	22537	221	Pan American	N365PA	23 Sep 81
1721	22490	257	Republic AL	N719RC	12 Feb 81	1780	22664	264	Mexicana	XA-MXD	29 Sep 81
1722	22349	233	Air Canada	C-GYNI	23 Feb 81	1781	22554	225	Eastern AL	N817EA	5 Oct 81
1723	22375	2D6	Air Algerie	7T-VEW	27 Feb 81	1782	22538	221	Pan American	N366PA	8 Dec 81
1724	22290	228	Air France	F-GCDI	25 Feb 81	1783	22555	225	Eastern AL	N818EA	15 Oct 81
1725	22166	243	Alitalia	I-DIRQ	27 Feb 81	1784	22687	2X8	Wistair Int	N4523N	21 Oct 81
1726	22491	257	Republic AL	N720RC	6 Mar 81	1785	22677	264	Delta AL	N546DA	27 Oct 81
1727	22608	2X3	Air Charter Int	F-GCMV	4 Mar 81	1786	22665	2H9	JAT	YU-AKK	2 Nov 81
1728	22413	264	Mexicana	XA-MEL	9 Mar 81	1787	22605	287	Aero Argentinas	LV-OLP	6 Nov 81
1729	22492	257	Republic AL	N721RC	17 Mar 81	1788	22763	269	Kuwait AW	9K-AFD	12 Nov 81
1730	22532	247	Western AL	N295WA	13 Mar 81	1789	22759	260	Ethiopian AL	ET-AHK	18 Nov 81
1731	22609	2X3	Air Charter Int	F-GCMX	20 Mar 81	1790	22666	2H9	JAT	YU-AKL	18 Nov 81
1732	22603	287	Aero Argentinas	LV-OLN	25 Mar 81	1791	22621	233	Air Canada	C-GYNK	25 Jan 82
1733	22574	2J4	Sterling AW	OY-SBG	20 Mar 81	1792	22622	233	Air Canada	C-GYNL	8 Feb 82
1734	22548	225	Eastern AL	N811EA	31 Mar 81	1793	22556	225	Eastern AL	N819EA	12 Mar 82
1735	22163	2B7	US Air	N771AL	27 Mar 81	1794	22539	221	Pan American	N367PA	26 Jan 82
1736	22533	247	Western AL	N296WA	8 Apr 81	1795	22557	225	Eastern AL	N820EA	17 Mar 82
1737	22549	225	Eastern AL	N812EA	9 Apr 81	1796	22540	221	Pan American	N368PA	16 Apr 82
1738	22534	247	Western AL	N297WA	2 Apr 81	1797	22541	221	Pan American	N369PA	16 Apr 82
1739	22550	225	Eastern AL	N813EA	16 Apr 81	1798	22558	225	Eastern AL	N821EA	9 Apr 82
1740	22448	224	Continental AL	N79745	9 Apr 81	1799	22542	221	Pan American	N370PA	16 Apr 82
1741	22493	232	Delta AL	N544DA	14 Apr 81	1800	22559	225	Eastern AL	N822EA	13 Apr 82
1742	22459	223	American AL	N701AA	21 Apr 81	1801	22765	206	Air Algerie	7T-VEX	20 Apr 82
1743	22164	2B7	US Air	N772AL	20 Apr 81	1802	22982	264	Dubai Gov	A6-HHM	5 May 82
1744	22551	225	Eastern AL	N814EA	27 Apr 81	1803	22623	233	Air Canada	C-GYNM	12 May 82
1745	22350	233	Air Canada	C-GYNJ	24 Apr 81	1804	22992	2F2	THY	TC-JCA	24 May 82
1746	22460	223	American AL	N702AA	1 May 81	1805	22825	2N6	Nigerian Gov	5N-AGY	4 Jun 82
1747	22476	259	Avianca	N205AV	6 May 81	1806	22983	264	US Air	N773AL	18 Nov 82
1748	22414	264	Mexicana	XA-MEM	4 May 81	1807	22770	2K3	US Air	N776AL	28 Jun 82
1749	22494	232	Delta AL	N545DA	11 May 81	1808	22993	2F2	THY	TC-JCB	8 Jul 82
1750	22461	223	American AL	N703AA	13 May 81	1809	22263	270	Iraqi AW	YI-AGS	15 Jul 82
1751	22462	223	American AL	N705AA	12 May 81	1810	22998	2F2	THY	TC-JCC	10 Aug 82
1752	22167	243	Alitalia	I-DIRR	20 May 81	1811	22999	2F2	THY	TC-JCD	25 Aug 82
1753	22641	277	Ansett AL	VH-ANA	29 May 81	1812	22606	287	Aero Argentinas	LV-OLR	1 Sep 82
1754	22676	264	Mexicana	XA-MEZ	20 May 81	1813	22984	264	US Air	N774AL	19 Nov 82
1755	22463	223	American AL	N706AA	18 May 81	1814	22702	243	Alitalia	I-DIRT	9 Nov 82
1756	22449	224	Continental AL	N79746	2 Jun 81	1815	22968	2Y4	Rafi Hariri	HZ-RH3	15 Dec 82
1757	22661	264	Mexicana	XA-MXA	29 May 81	1816	23014	264	US Air	N775AL	26 Jan 83
1758	22464	223	American AL	N707AA	2 Jun 81	1817	23052	270	US Air	N779AL	23 Mar 83
1759	22642	277	Ansett AL	VH-ANB	4 Jun 81	1818	22924	2S2F	Fed Express	N201FE	28 Apr 83
1760	22450	224	Continental AL	N79748	4 Jun 81	1819	22925	2S2F	Fed Express	N203FE	24 May 83
1761	22465	223	American AL	N708AA	10 Jun 81	1820	22926	2S2F	Fed Express	N204FE	8 Jul 83
1762	22643	277	Ansett AL	VH-ANE	18 Jun 81	1821	22927	2S2F	Fed Express	N205FE	5 Aug 83
1763	22466	223	American AL	N709AA	16 Jun 81	1822	22928	2S2F	Fed Express	N206FE	1 Sep 83
1764	22535	221	Pan American	N363PA	23 Jun 81	1823	22929	2S2F	Fed Express	N207FE	7 Oct 83
1765	22467	223	American AL	N710AA	26 Jun 81	1824	22930	2S2F	Fed Express	N208FE	9 Nov 83
1766	22468	223	American AL	N712AA	25 Jun 81	1825	22931	2S2F	Fed Express	N209FE	19 Dec 83
1767	22451	224	Continental AL	N79749	6 Jul 81	1826	22932	2S2F	Fed Express	N210FE	30 Jan 84
1768	22644	277	Ansett AL	VH-ANF	8 Jul 81	1827	22933	2S2F	Fed Express	N211FE	2 Mar 84
1769	22469	223	American AL	N713AA	14 Jul 81	1828	22934	2S2F	Fed Express	N212FE	4 Apr 84
1770	22168	246	Alitalia	I-DIRS	3 Aug 81	1829	22935	2S2F	Fed Express	N213FE	9 May 84
1771	22470	223	American AL	N715AA	7 Aug 81	1830	22936	2S2F	Fed Express	N215FE	12 Jun 84
1772	22452	224	Continental AL	N79750	13 Aug 81	1831	22937	2S2F	Fed Express	N216FE	24 Jul 84
1773	22552	225	Eastern AL	N815EA	19 Aug 81	1832	22938	2S2F	Fed Express	N217FE	28 Aug 84

Above:
The break-up of the Soviet Union and its buffer territories has opened a whole new market for western jets — especially the more-affordable second-hand variety. Air Terrex was established in 1992, and now operates several 727-100s on holiday services from the Czech Republic to areas around the Mediterranean and North Africa.
Hugh Newell

Below:
Ansett's revised colour scheme was introduced in 1981, and was first seen on VH-ANA — one of the final batch of 727-200s built for service in Australia. These late-standard aircraft were fitted with 15,500lb thrust JT8D-15 engines and long-range tanks, which allowed them to operate unrestricted Sydney-Perth sectors at any time of the year.